INDIANS

POCAHONTAS, *Seymour*
SACAGAWEA, *Seymour*
SEQUOYAH, *Snow*
SITTING BULL, *Stevenson*
SQUANTO, *Stevenson*
TECUMSEH, *Stevenson*

NAVAL HEROES

DAVID FARRAGUT, *Long*
GEORGE DEWEY, *Long*
JOHN PAUL JONES, *Snow*
MATTHEW CALBRAITH PERRY, *Scharbach*
OLIVER HAZARD PERRY, *Long*
RAPHAEL SEMMES, *Snow*
STEPHEN DECATUR, *Smith*

NOTED WIVES and MOTHERS

ABIGAIL ADAMS, *Wagoner*
DOLLY MADISON, *Monsell*
JESSIE FREMONT, *Wagoner*
MARTHA WASHINGTON, *Wagoner*
MARY TODD LINCOLN, *Wilkie*
NANCY HANKS, *Stevenson*
RACHEL JACKSON, *Govan*

SCIENTISTS and INVENTORS

ALBERT EINSTEIN, *Hammontree*
ALECK BELL, *Widdemer*
CYRUS MCCORMICK, *Dobler*
ELI WHITNEY, *Snow*
ELIAS HOWE, *Corcoran*
ELIZABETH BLACKWELL, *Henry*
GEORGE CARVER, *Stevenson*
GEORGE EASTMAN, *Henry*
HENRY FORD, *Aird and Ruddiman*
JOHN AUDUBON, *Mason*
LUTHER BURBANK, *Burt*
MARIA MITCHELL, *Melin*
ROBERT FULTON, *Henry*
SAMUEL MORSE, *Snow*
TOM EDISON, *Guthridge*
WALTER REED, *Higgins*
WILBUR AND ORVILLE WRIGHT, *Stevenson*
WILL AND CHARLIE MAYO, *Hammontree*

SOCIAL and CIVIC LEADERS

BETSY ROSS, *Weil*
BOOKER T. WASHINGTON,
  Stevenson
CLARA BARTON, *Stevenson*
DAN BEARD, *Mason*
FRANCES WILLARD, *Mason*
JANE ADDAMS, *Wagoner*
J. STERLING MORTON, *Moore*
JULIA WARD HOWE, *Wagoner*
JULIETTE LOW, *Higgins*
LILIUOKALANI, *Newman*
LUCRETIA MOTT, *Burnett*
MOLLY PITCHER, *Stevenson*
OLIVER WENDELL HOLMES, JR.,
  Dunham
SUSAN ANTHONY, *Monsell*

SOLDIER

ANTHONY WAYNE, *Stevenson*
BEDFORD FORREST, *Parks*
DAN MORGAN, *Bryant*
ETHAN ALLEN, *Winders*
FRANCIS MARION, *Steele*
ISRAEL PUTNAM, *Stevenson*
JEB STUART, *Winders*
NATHANAEL GREENE, *Peckham*
ROBERT E. LEE, *Monsell*
SAM HOUSTON, *Stevenson*
TOM JACKSON, *Monsell*
U. S. GRANT, *Stevenson*
WILLIAM HENRY HARRISON,
  Peckham
ZACK TAYLOR, *Wilkie*

STATESMEN

ABE LINCOLN, *Stevenson*
ANDY JACKSON, *Stevenson*
DAN WEBSTER, *Smith*
FRANKLIN ROOSEVELT, *Weil*
HENRY CLAY, *Monsell*
JAMES MONROE, *Widdemer*
JEFF DAVIS, *de Grummond
  and Delaune*
JOHN MARSHALL, *Monsell*
TEDDY ROOSEVELT, *Parks*
WOODROW WILSON, *Monsell*

Will Clark

Boy in Buckskins

Illustrated by William Moyers

Will Clark

Boy in Buckskins

By Katharine E. Wilkie

THE **BOBBS-MERRILL** COMPANY, INC.
A SUBSIDIARY OF HOWARD W. SAMS & CO., INC.
Publishers • INDIANAPOLIS • NEW YORK

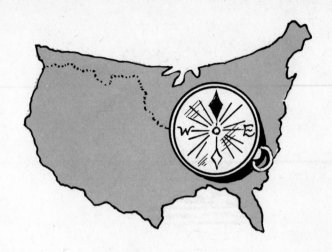

*This book is proudly dedicated
to
my mother and father*

Illustrations

Full pages

Numerous smaller illustrations

Contents

Books by Katharine E. Wilkie

GEORGE ROGERS CLARK: BOY OF THE OLD NORTHWEST

MARY TODD LINCOLN: GIRL OF THE BLUEGRASS

SIMON KENTON: YOUNG TRAIL BLAZER

WILL CLARK: BOY IN BUCKSKINS

WILLIAM FARGO: YOUNG MAIL CARRIER

ZACH TAYLOR: YOUNG ROUGH AND READY

★ ★ Will Clark

Boy in Buckskins

Tracking the Trader

"WHO-O-O! WHO-O-O!" The man with the heavy oilskin pack on his back shivered as he walked along through the pine woods. He looked up at the tall trees. He knew what the hoot owl might mean if he were back in Kentucky. In this year 1777 it could be the disguised voice of an Indian. He shifted his pack and walked a little faster.

From overhead a pair of laughing blue eyes looked down through the branches at Trader Jenkins. A seven-year-old boy with fiery red hair was hidden in the treetop.

Again the boy gave the call: "Who-o-o!"

The traveler disappeared around a bend in the trail. Will Clark slid down the trunk of the tree and ran after him. Not a twig crackled. Not a leaf stirred. Will knew how to move quietly through the forest.

He ran up a hill. Now he had almost caught up with Trader Jenkins. The man did not suspect that anyone was near. Will fixed his eyes on a distant sycamore tree. At least a hundred yards lay between him and the man. The trees were close together here. They hid Will from Trader Jenkins.

Finally the traveler reached the sycamore and walked under it. Will waited eagerly. Nothing happened. Then——

"Caw-w-w! Caw-w-w!"

Trader Jenkins looked up. Several black crows were circling above his head. They rose and dipped in the air.

Will peeped out from behind the tree trunk.

He grinned as he saw the traveler's puzzled face. He knew what the man was thinking. Trader Jenkins imagined that the sound might come from an Indian's throat.

Soon the trader disappeared over the hill. Will ran to the foot of the sycamore tree. He looked up into its branches. A boy slid down the trunk and landed at his feet.

"Was I all right?" the boy asked him. "Did I sound like a crow?"

"You were perfect, Jack," declared Will Clark. "If you had come flapping down on two black wings, I wouldn't have been surprised."

Jack laughed. "I wouldn't talk, you red-headed rascal. You fooled him, too."

Will gave him a friendly punch. "Never mind my hair. Let's listen. The trader should be near Randy by this time."

The boys bent their heads and listened. From a distance they heard a sound—"Gr-r-r!"—soft at first, then louder. "Gr-r-r!" Most people would have thought it was the growl of a wolf.

Will gave a satisfied nod. "That's Randy. Regular old wolf, isn't he?"

Jack grinned. "Some people might think so. The trader seems to. Anyhow, our signals are working, Will."

"Of course they are! They have to work. Every fellow is doing his part. It's perfect team-work. Let's hurry. I want to see where Trader Jenkins is going."

A little farther along they were joined by a third boy. Will threw a friendly arm across his shoulders. "You sounded just like a wolf."

"He must have reached the last lookout by now," said Randy. "He'll soon be at the fork in the road."

The three boys listened intently. A sound rang out into the still evening: "Gobble-gobble-gobble! Gobble-gobble-gobble!"

14

The three boys bent double with laughter. They could imagine a plump, red-faced Joel gobbling like a wild turkey from a treetop while the lonely traveler plodded along beneath him.

Will strained his eyes to see through the shadows. "Why, the man's going toward our house!" he exclaimed.

"I wish it were our house," grumbled Jack. "He may have news of the war."

"Or of the Kentucky settlements," Randy said. "He might have come from there."

"Or even George," Will added. "I hope he can tell us about George."

The other boys knew that George Rogers Clark was Will's brother in Kentucky, far across the blue wall of mountains. He was in the fort at Harrodstown. They knew, too, that George's family had not seen him for more than a year —since 1776, when he had come from Kentucky to Virginia for powder. The settlers needed it to defend their homes from the British and the Indians. At first the governor had not wanted to give him the powder. But at last George had taken it back across the mountains with him.

"I'm going home, boys," said Will. "Tell Joel and Harry we will do some more tracking in a few days."

He was off like a flash toward the rambling farmhouse where his family lived. It was on the top of a hill in eastern Virginia near the Tidewater region. With good luck he could reach home before Trader Jenkins arrived there.

Will ran like a deer. The deepening twilight did not stop him. He knew every tree, stump, rock, and path in the countryside.

Now he had reached the entrance to Stony Cave. He looked back. He could see the trader behind him. Will ran on. Now he was passing the ruins of the old burned cabin, and here was the chinquapin grove.

Here, too, was the fence row of mulberry trees. Now he was really home. There was the house rising up from the darkness. Lights were shining from the windows.

He knew where to look for his mother. Ann Clark was always near the kitchen at mealtime.

He thought of his five sturdy, hungry older brothers. Jonathan, John, Richard, and Edmund were fighting in the Continental Army in Virginia. George was on the Kentucky frontier. Will was proud that all of them were helping to free the colonies from the yoke of England. He wished he were old enough to fight.

Now only his mother and father, his four sisters, and he were left at home to sit about the wide dining table.

"Trader Jenkins is coming, Mother," Will called from the door.

"He will be welcome," Ann Clark said. She liked the little man who came through the neighborhood once or twice a year. "I need some pins and buttons. Will, you look so much like your brother George that I almost thought you were he for a moment."

"Do I?" the boy asked. He seemed pleased.

His mother smiled. "You have the same features, the same red hair, and the same blue eyes. At your age he looked as much like you as one pea looks like another."

But Will was thinking about something else. "We followed the trader all the way from Poynter's Creek."

She gave a little cry. "Poynter's Creek! That's a good five miles away."

"I know it. We trailed him every step of the way, and he never saw us even once. We wanted to see if we could do it."

"We?" asked Ann Clark.

"Jack, Randy, Joel, Harry, and I," Will told her. "I wish we were old enough to be in the army. Surely General Washington could use some good spies like us."

"Don't worry or be in a hurry," Ann Clark said. "This awful war will be over someday, and we will be a free people. Then we'll have to protect our freedom. Our country will need you as much in twenty years as she needs men now—maybe even more."

An Unexpected Arrival

"THIS IS THE best meal I've eaten for months, ma'am," said Abraham Jenkins as he pushed his chair back from the table.

The Clarks were finishing supper. Ann Clark had prepared fried chicken, spoon bread, tender young green beans, and hominy grits for their visitor. She had opened a jar of her best spiced peach pickle.

"We have the best food in Virginia," Will told the trader.

"Why, Billy!" exclaimed his mother. Her cheeks were pink.

"Perhaps the lad is right." His father laughed.

"I'm sure our other sons would agree with him. I certainly do."

"I wish they were here to share our supper tonight," said Ann Clark sadly.

"You still have one boy at home," Will reminded her. "I'm afraid the war will be over before I'm old enough to be in the army."

John and Ann Clark exchanged glances across the table.

"I pray it will end soon with victory for our side," said Will's father.

"I don't care too much about fighting," Will admitted. "I'd rather be a scout and explore new country. I wish I could go back to Kentucky with you, Mr. Jenkins."

The trader reached over and pinched the boy's ear. "You must wait a few years, Will," he said. "There will still be plenty of land to explore when you are grown."

Will hitched his chair closer to their guest.

21

"What is the Kentucky wilderness like?" he asked eagerly.

Abraham Jenkins laughed. "You've heard the old song, haven't you? The one that goes:

"The bear went over the mountain,
The bear went over the mountain,
The bear went over the mountain,
To see what he could see!"

Will and the girls laughed as the weather-beaten little man sang the words in a high, squeaky voice. Trader Jenkins smiled back at them.

"What did he find?" Will demanded.

"T'other side of the mountain,
T'other side of the mountain,
T'other side of the mountain,
Was all that he could see!"

"Aw, shucks." Will looked disappointed. His sisters laughed again.

Mr. Jenkins spoke quickly. "I shouldn't have teased you, lad. I'm sorry. At first the Kentucky wilderness looks very much like the Virginia wilderness. Then little by little the mountains level out. By the time you come to Harrodstown, the land is smooth and rolling. Kentucky's a great country, Will. A man may hunt and fish to his heart's content there, unless he gets an arrow in his back."

"Why can't the settlers make friends with the Indians?" asked Will. "Isn't there room enough for both?"

Trader Jenkins shrugged his shoulders. "Well, the Indians don't seem to think so. Neither do some of the settlers. You might ask your brother George."

"What might he ask his brother George?" asked a deep voice from the doorway.

Everyone looked up quickly. A tall young man of twenty-five in frontiersman's clothes

stood smiling at them. Mrs. Clark turned pale
with surprise.

"George!" screamed the girls.

Will and Lucy hurried over to him. Four-
year-old Fanny scampered after them.

John Clark pushed back his chair and hurried to greet his son. "Welcome home, George!" he exclaimed. "We're glad to see you!"

The tall young man in buckskins shook hands with his father, kissed his mother and sisters, and gave a friendly nod to Abraham Jenkins. Then he sat down beside Will and rumpled his brother's hair with his firm, brown fingers.

"Are you surprised to see me, Redhead?" he asked with a smile.

"We had your message some weeks ago. You said you might come next month," said Ann Clark. "What brings you sooner, my son?"

George did not answer at once. He rose and walked up and down the room. There was a deep frown on his young forehead. "I have some business at Williamsburg," he said at last. "I wish the Kentucky country were not so far away from the capital of Virginia. The journey across the mountains is long and dangerous.

But it's the only way to reach the governor. And I must see him at once."

"Let me go back to Kentucky with you, George," Will begged.

George did not seem to hear him. He leaned against the chimney piece for a moment. He was thinking deeply.

Will's mouth drooped. "I know what your answer will be: No!"

George spoke sharply. "Those are the words of a child, Will. Of course my answer must be no!"

"When may I come?" Will demanded.

"When you're old enough," his brother promised. "Not before."

Will's blue eyes were afire with excitement. "You really mean that?"

George nodded. "It's a promise."

Will turned to their father. "Will he keep his word, Father?"

John Clark nodded. "A Clark always keeps his word."

George reached out a long arm and drew the boy over to him. "Besides, any agreement between two redheads is binding. Would you like to come through the Cumberland Gap or down the Ohio River?"

Will's voice shook with excitement. "I don't care how I come just as long as I get there. Shall I have buckskins and high leather boots like yours, George?"

His brother nodded. "You shall. And here's a knife to seal the bargain."

He drew a wide-bladed hunting knife from the sheath at his belt. He presented it with a flourish to his young brother.

"It's really mine?" the boy asked.

"It really is," George assured him.

"But, George," their mother began anxiously, "do you really think——"

"It's not sharp enough to hurt him if he's careful," the older son told her. "Will is old enough to own a knife, and I'll buy myself a new one at Williamsburg. It's time for him to learn how to use one. He might have to fight a few Indians when he comes to Kentucky."

Will's eyes were troubled. "Suppose I don't want to fight Indians. I might prefer to make friends with them."

John Clark burst into a hearty laugh. "He might at that. The lad is fast friends with everyone in Caroline County. He knows them all— rich and poor, old and young."

"It's a good way to be," George said gently. "A man needs friends. But he must learn to protect himself, too, in case of danger."

A Dangerous Adventure

It was a hot July afternoon. Will and York were playing with a tame chipmunk. York was the cook's son. He was nine years old. That was nearly a year older than Will. He was Will's special friend.

Often Jack and Randy Johnson came over from a neighboring plantation. Sometimes Joel and Harry Smith, who lived nearer Fredericksburg, came, too. But today Will and York were playing alone.

York poked at the chipmunk with a small stick. "He would make a nice little pelt if you killed him and skinned him."

Will shook his head. "No. I don't mind killing animals if I see any reason for it. But why should I kill this one? Besides, I want to show him to Elizabeth. She'll be home tomorrow from her visit."

"Maybe she'd like to see one of those red lizards that live in Stony Cave," suggested York. His eyes twinkled with mischief. "Do you think she would?"

Will chuckled outright. "Perhaps she'd like us to drop one down her neck."

Both boys went into a gale of laughter. "Wouldn't she be wild?" York said.

"Girls are so silly," Will added. "Elizabeth isn't as silly as most of them."

"So you think girls are silly," his father said from behind him.

The boys turned around quickly. Will's face was red. He wondered how much his father had heard. He did not think John Clark would ap-

approve of their dropping a lizard down Elizabeth's back.

"For your information they aren't lizards," said John Clark. "They are salamanders."

That finished it. He *had* heard them talking. Will waited for a lecture.

"You certainly know a lot about animals, Mr. Clark," said York. "You know even their book names. I don't see how you do it."

Will grinned. York was doing his best to out-talk John Clark.

"York's right, Father," Will said. "How did you learn so much?"

John Clark smiled. He know what the boys were attempting to do. "I once knew a boy back in Albemarle County who interested me in the study of plants and animals," he said. "His name was Thomas Jefferson. He owned many fine books with pictures of animals from every part of the world."

"I wish I knew him," said Will. "I'd like to see those books."

"He knows you," said his father. "We went back to our old neighborhood to visit relatives when you were a baby. We saw Tom Jefferson again. He said: 'Take care of that little redhead. A redhead may grow up to be a useful man.' His eyes were twinkling as he talked. Jefferson himself has red hair, you know."

"So has my brother George," Will said proudly. "Just like mine."

"Tom Jefferson collects plants and animals," Mr. Clark told the boys. "He lives in a beautiful house which he himself designed. He calls it Monticello—Little Mountain—for the high hill on which it stands."

"We could make a collection," Will suggested. "I don't care so much about plants as I do about animals, but we could have both, I guess."

York nodded eagerly. "There's my pet crow."

"And the tame squirrel."

"And the young robin with the broken wing."

"This will be fun!" Will exclaimed.

"Don't forget a salamander or so," John Clark added slyly. "I'd put them in a jar or a box—not down Elizabeth's neck."

The boys laughed and scampered away. He did not intend to scold them after all.

Half an hour later down in the orchard the boys looked at their collection of animals. There was the chipmunk. There was the tame crow. There was the robin.

The boys had added a mother cat and her three kittens. She did not want to stay. She insisted on picking up her babies by the back of their soft little necks. One by one she carried them back to the porch.

"Let her go," said Will disgustedly. "She's only a silly old cat anyway. I don't think she likes us very much."

"We need more animals," York said mournfully. "What shall we do?"

Will nodded. Their collection was too small. Suddenly his blue eyes lighted up. "I know! We should have Star."

Star was the two-week-old calf. Will and York went at least twice a day to see him. He was a cunning little long-legged fellow with big brown eyes. He was still wobbly on his thin legs.

The boys dashed toward the south meadow. Star was standing near the gate. His mother was grazing at the far end of the field.

Will threw a rope around the calf's neck. Before Star knew what was happening, the boys had pulled him through the gate in the direction of the orchard.

"I must have dropped my lucky rabbit's foot back in the meadow," panted York. "Can you manage Star alone for a minute?"

Will nodded. He did not have too much

breath left. Star was stronger than he had expected. The little animal was twisting and turning like a mad creature. He was giving out pitiful sounds that made Will wince.

York ran back toward the meadow. He did not stop to open the gate. To save time he went over the top. He must find that rabbit's foot.

Meanwhile Will tightened his hold on the rope. Why must Star make such a fuss? If he'd just behave, it wouldn't hurt him.

"Help!"

The frightened cry rang out from the meadow. Will looked back in that direction. York was standing stock-still in the center of the field. Old Bess had missed her calf. With head lowered she was charging at York.

Will had never seen her angry before. Usually she was mild and gentle. But now he noticed only her ugly horns and her threatening head. She looked savage.

York was too frightened to move. He stood still as a statue. Will had no time to think. He went into action.

In the twinkling of an eye he tore across the yard. In one bound he leaped over the gate. Old Bess was charging on. Another moment and she would toss York on her sharp horns.

Will snatched off his jacket. He sprang in front of Bess. He waved the garment before her. The startled cow stopped for a moment.

"Run, York, run!" Will shouted.

The Negro boy took to his heels. He ran like the wind. Over the gate he scrambled. He fell in a heap on the other side.

Old Bess tossed her head. Will shook the jacket in front of her again. He measured with his eyes the distance between himself and a low-limbed apple tree.

The next instant he took to his heels. He ran faster than he had ever run in his whole life. He

did not dare to look back. He went up the tree as though he were a squirrel.

At last he was safe on an overhanging limb. He looked down. Old Bess stood almost beneath him. She no longer seemed so angry. Now and then she gave a mournful bellow. Will felt almost sorry for her.

Soon John Clark came into sight. He was leading Star. York trailed along behind them. His head hung down as though he were ashamed of himself.

Father opened the gate and led Star through. The calf trotted over to his mother. She licked him happily. Then Bess and Star turned and ambled down to the far end of the meadow.

Father waited for Will to come down from the tree. He said nothing at first. His face was stern.

When Will was going through the gate, John Clark spoke. "She was only protecting her calf."

Late that afternoon Will stole down alone to

the meadow with a bucket of bran mash. He lifted it across the fence. Bess came to get it. Will reached through the bars and patted her sleek brown neck.

"I'm sorry, Bess," he told her. "I'm really sorry. I didn't mean to hurt him."

Then he petted the calf.

A Ride in the Night

IT WAS 1779. Will Clark had grown into a tall boy of nine. Today he stood facing his father in the dining room of their Virginia home.

"He's too young," Ann Clark said quickly to her husband.

John Clark frowned. He was sitting in a big armchair with one foot on a stool in front of him. He looked hard at Will. "Yes, he's too young," John Clark agreed.

"But I can do it, Father," Will Clark said.

"Those horses must be delivered," Mr. Clark said slowly.

"But he's only a boy, John," his wife insisted.

Mr. Clark looked at Will. Few boys of his age were as tall and as broad-shouldered as this red-haired, blue-eyed lad. He could easily have been mistaken for eleven.

"This boy can do it," John Clark answered at last. "I know he can."

Will could hardly keep back a shout. He was really going to be trusted with the job.

"Listen carefully to me," said John Clark. "You must carry out my directions to the letter. Oh, if only I had not dropped that stone on my foot last week!"

"Don't worry, Father," said Will. "I'll do exactly as you say."

John Clark's voice dropped almost to a whisper. "You'll take the string of six horses to the ford at Plover's Creek. There you'll cross and follow the trail to Sugar Maple Hill. On the far side of the hill is a small tavern run by a man named Coleman. I've never seen him, so I can't describe him to you. But the password is 'Kentucky,' so don't give the horses to anyone who doesn't give it to you."

"Kentucky!"

"Hush!" commanded John Clark. "What better password is there for a man with a son on the Kentucky frontier?"

"And we'll go there someday," Will reminded him. "You promised, and so did George."

His father nodded. "Meanwhile you must get those horses delivered. They'll be used in the Continental Army. General Washington needs them. He needs all the help every patriot can give. Take York with you. Sometimes two heads are better than one."

Will started out of the room on a run. His mother called him back. She looked at her youngest son for a long time. "Now I have six sons serving their country," she said softly.

Fifteen minutes later Will and York were riding away from home in the moonlight. Besides their own mounts, they had six horses to be delivered to Coleman's Inn.

Neither boy knew too well the part of the country to which he was going. But Will was certain he could find the place.

"You must be part bloodhound." York chuckled. "I'll bet you could find your way to Kentucky all by yourself."

"I'd like to try," Will answered. "But by the time I go, the route will be well marked."

"I won't mind if it is," said York. "You'll take me with you, won't you?"

"Of course. When the war is over, all of us are going. All my family and all yours. We'll make quite a procession, won't we? By that time my five brothers will be home from the army. I suppose they'll go, too. And, of course, there are Elizabeth, Lucy, Fanny, and Ann."

"I wish we were there now in a nice, warm

house. It's cold out here tonight," said York with a shiver. His teeth chattered as he spoke. Somewhere in the distance a hoot owl gave a mournful sound. "Listen!"

"At least you know that's not an Indian on the warpath. All the Indians in Virginia are friendly ones," said Will. "Do you remember how the other boys and I used to imitate Indian calls and follow every traveler who came through the woods near home?"

"Yes, I do," York answered. "Look. Yonder is the ford."

In the distance Plover's Creek flowed peacefully in the moonlight. The boys had been riding for several hours. They were glad to come to this stage in their journey. The path to the ford lay clear and shining before them.

"Come on!" called Will. He kicked his horse's sides slightly. "You follow behind, York, just to be certain everything is all right."

In a few minutes the boys rode up out of the water. The wet coats of the horses shone in the moonlight. The trail toward Sugar Maple Hill was clearly to be seen.

Will shivered slightly. "That water was chilly. I'll be glad to deliver these horses and warm myself before a good fire."

York sighed. "It seems as if I can taste Mama's bacon and hominy grits right now. I'm hungry."

"So am I," agreed his companion. "It can't be much longer now, York."

AT THE TAVERN

Nearly an hour later the boys looked down from a little rise into the valley below. They saw a large tavern. Smoke was curling from the chimney even though the hour was early.

"There's our breakfast," York said hungrily. "What are we waiting for?"

"I don't know," Will said slowly. "There's something I don't like. I'm not certain what it is. Look, York." He pointed toward a half-dozen horses tied outside the tavern. "Father said I should see a man. There's more than one man in that tavern."

"Well, after all, people do spend the night at taverns," York reminded him.

Will frowned. "Maybe I'm being extra careful—but I'm not going to take these horses down there yet. You lead them back into the woods and wait for me."

"All right," York grumbled. "But don't forget my stomach has just about grown to my backbone. I'm hungry!"

York turned with the horses and led them into the surrounding woods. Will rode alone down to the tavern.

He dismounted outside the door. Then he tied his mare to the hitching rack with the other horses. His heart was beating fast as he entered the building.

Once inside the main room he looked quickly about him. What he feared was true: a group of red-coated soldiers were sitting around a large pine table.

"Here's a new man for King George!" one of them called loudly.

Will swallowed hard as they turned to look at him. The British soldiers with their mugs and platters looked as big as giants. The landlord leaned over the counter. He had a long, sharp carving knife in his hand.

The boy tried to speak. For a moment his voice would not come. "I d-don't think the King could use me yet," he stammered.

Most of the men roared with laughter. They seemed to think the idea of Will as a soldier was very funny.

"He doesn't think the King could use him

yet!" repeated one of the men. "He's right. King George doesn't want fighters as young as he is. Ha! Ha! Ha!"

Another soldier was watching Will closely. This man had not laughed so much as his companions. "What are you doing out so early, boy?" he demanded.

Will gave a start. He hoped the man did not notice it. He did some fast thinking. "I'm on my way to my aunt's house, sir."

"Where does she live?" asked the soldier. He kept his eyes fixed on Will.

"At Williamsburg."

"And you're going there alone?"

"There's no one to go with me. I'm an orphan. I spend half the time with my aunt and the other half with my grandmother down in the country," Will added.

He stole a glance at the other men. They were paying little attention to him. They were too busy talking and laughing and eating. Then the questioning soldier turned to them. "This boy may know something about the horses."

Will's heart was in his mouth. He had been right after all: there was something wrong here somewhere.

The man was still talking. "He may even have brought them with him."

"Nonsense, Brown!" insisted another man. "He's only a boy. No one would trust valuable horses to a boy."

The soldier called Brown turned toward Will. His eyes were cold and dangerous. He twisted Will's shoulder cruelly. "We're on the lookout for horses intended for the Continental Army. Do you know anything about them?"

"Ouch! You're hurting me."

The man's roughness had brought real tears to Will's eyes. The boy was glad of it. The pain would excuse the look of fear on his face. But his great fear was for York, hidden back in the woods with the horses.

"Stop it, Brown," one of the men ordered. "I have a son at home about his age. You sha'n't mistreat this boy."

Brown scowled. "Even boys can be traitors. How do I know he isn't a lying little rebel?"

"Shut up, I tell you!" said the other soldier. "This lad knows nothing about any horses. Eat your breakfast, boy, and be on your way."

Will could hardly swallow the plate of ham and eggs which the innkeeper brought him. This man, too, gave him a keen look that did nothing to relieve his uneasiness. Could he be the Mr. Coleman of whom his father had spoken? It didn't seem so from the way he scowled. He didn't look friendly at all.

As soon as Will had finished, he laid a coin on the table and stole out the door. Once astride his mare, he turned her head toward the woods.

"That's not the road to Williamsburg," growled a voice from the doorway.

The boy looked down to meet the scowling eyes of his enemy. "I was only getting my bearings," he explained. "I know the road to Williamsburg."

He galloped off in the opposite direction from the one he wanted to take. York must wait with the horses. Will hoped with all his heart that the Negro boy would remain hidden in the woods.

Once out of sight of the tavern, Will slid out of the saddle. He patted the mare's muzzle and led her off the road into the underbrush. "We won't have a trail to follow this time, girl," he told her. "But somehow we must get back to York and those horses."

The distance back was short. But the going was rough. The way was tangled with sharp briers and thick undergrowth. Several times Will became a little confused.

Finally, however, he came to the spot where York sat in a little clearing. Will drew a breath of relief when he saw him. The horses were standing quietly near by.

"I thought you had deserted me," York moaned. "I thought I'd have to stay out here in these woods until I starved to death."

"That might be better than a rope around your neck," Will told him grimly. "That tavern is filled with British soldiers. I had trouble getting away from them."

York's eyes opened wide. "What shall we do now?" he asked.

"We must wait for them to leave," Will said. "We'll take turns watching. They'll have to be on their way before long."

The sun was high in the sky before the soldiers came out the tavern door. They mounted their horses and galloped away toward the north. The boys waited in the woods a while longer.

At last they made their way slowly and cautiously down to the tavern.

The landlord's face lighted up with a smile as Will came in the door.

"So it's you again," he said. "You wouldn't be from Kentucky, would you?"

He said the word so loudly and clearly that Will knew he had come to the end of his journey.

"No, I'm not from Kentucky," he answered. He, too, lingered on the word. "Neither are my horses hidden back in the woods. But maybe you'd like to have them anyway."

The landlord gave a hearty laugh. He laid a friendly hand on Will's shoulder. "That I would," he said. "I've been looking for them. And my son Edward will take them on their way tonight. My name is George Coleman."

Will gave a happy sigh. He had completed his mission successfully. He had finished the job. Now he could go home.

"I thought it was all over when you walked in on the King's men," said Mr. Coleman. "It wasn't safe for me to give you a signal of any kind. But you played your part well. You're a bright lad—a lad to help build America."

Will smiled happily as he and York rode away from the tavern toward home. He was proud because of Mr. Coleman's praise. But most of all he was proud because he had done something to help carry on the war.

Horse with Wings

"Nobody on the plantation will ever be able to ride that horse," John Clark prophesied. "He's too wild."

"I'd like to try," said Will. "Isn't he wonderful? Let's call him the Red One."

His father frowned. "He was sent here because he was too wild for army use. If grown men couldn't handle him, certainly a boy of ten couldn't manage him either."

Will said nothing, but he looked up at the big chestnut stallion standing in the paddock beyond the fence. The horse's red coat glistened in the sunlight. He tossed his head proudly.

The whites of his eyes flashed. The boy's heart leaped at the thought of riding such a magnificent animal.

"I doubt if this horse can ever be broken," said John Clark.

"George could break him," Will declared.

Mr. Clark laughed. "You think George can do anything, don't you?"

"He just about can," Will answered. "Look how he took the whole Northwest and then recaptured Vincennes in the dead of winter only last year. I'll bet the history books of the future will mention what happened in the year 1779."

"He's a Clark," said Will's father. "A Clark must never be found wanting in duty. When the time comes, may you do yours as well as George has done his!"

"I will, Father," Will promised. "You may depend on me."

Several times that day Will stole down to the

paddock where the big chestnut horse had been put. The last time Will climbed up on the high board fence. The stallion trumpeted and galloped to the far end of the enclosure.

"Easy, Red One, easy!" Will said. "I'm your friend, old fellow. I wish there were some way to make you believe it."

The animal stood quivering at the other end of the paddock. He turned his head slightly in Will's direction. The boy kept on talking. "I wouldn't hurt you for the world," he told the horse. "Come on over, Red. Let's get acquainted. Come here."

The enormous stallion stood without moving. His powerful sides rose and fell as he breathed. Will thought he had never seen so beautiful a sight in all his life. How he'd like to ride this animal! Months ago he had given his little mare to the army. Since then he had had no mount.

Slowly the boy extended a hand. In it was a

juicy red apple. He gave a little whistle of invitation. "Come and get it, Red," he coaxed. "It's all for you."

The horse pricked up his ears. Will's heart pounded. But the horse stood still. Nothing happened. A pang of disappointment ran over the waiting boy.

He still kept his hand extended. He hardly moved a muscle. He might have been a part of the fence. In this way he had made friends with many wild creatures of the woods and forest. Why wouldn't it work with the stallion?

After a long time the horse began to edge toward the boy. Will could hardly believe his eyes. He almost dropped the apple.

"That's it, Red!" he whispered. "Come on, boy. I'm your friend. I won't hurt you."

The big horse inched over to Will. There was a flash of big, white teeth, a pounding of hoofs, then the animal was over on the other side of the paddock. Will laughed heartily. This was the beginning of success.

Will climbed down and walked around the outside of the enclosure. He climbed up on the fence beside the horse. The Red One was still munching the apple.

The boy did not stop to think. In one swift move he leaped from the fence and swung himself over on the big horse's back.

There was no time to plan. The Red One gave a startled cry. Then he galloped to the other end of the paddock.

Will found himself flying through space as the horse cleared the five-foot fence in one mighty bound. Somehow he managed to hang on. He thought every second he would fall. He clung fast to the stallion's broad neck.

Trees, bushes, fences flew past. Will felt a thrill such as he had never felt before in all his life. He remembered the stories his father had told him of Pegasus, the winged horse of Greece. Well, he, Will Clark, was riding a winged horse right here in Virginia.

At the far end of the field stood a great oak tree. The Red One headed straight for it. Will gripped the horse's neck tighter. What would happen now?

For a second it looked as though the Red One with his rider would smash directly into the tree.

Will clung tightly, closed his eyes, and said a wordless prayer.

The horse was only inches away from the tree when he swerved. The sudden motion threw the boy to the ground.

"Well, what do you know!" he exclaimed.

He rose slowly and felt carefully for broken bones. In spite of his hard fall, he seemed to have no serious injuries. He looked in the direction of the stallion. By now Red One was grazing near the barn.

Will set his chin. "You wonderful creature! I'll ride you again if it's the last thing I do."

WILL DELIVERS A MESSAGE

A half hour later Will limped into the back door of the farmhouse. He expected a good scolding when his mother saw his muddy, torn clothes. Instead she and his father hardly noticed him. They were talking earnestly before the fireplace. Their voices were low.

"The message should be delivered at once," John Clark said. He had a worried frown on his face as he spoke.

"But it will be too late if you walk. And there are no good horses on the place."

Mr. Clark paced back and forth before the fire. "If that stallion could only be saddled! I should have kept at least one horse to ride. But I felt they should go to the army."

"What's wrong, Father?" asked Will.

John Clark looked at his son. "I've received a message from a trustworthy source which should be sent on at once. How can I send it? All our horses are too old and slow. Judge is lame and Rosie is nearly blind. The farm horses are no good. What shall I do? This message *must* go on."

"Where does it go?" asked Will.

"To the inn where you delivered the horses last year. There are rifles hidden in the churchyard at Breeze Hill. The British suspect the hiding place. They'll seize them tomorrow unless the proper persons are warned."

"Guns in the churchyard at Breeze Hill, and the British will seize them tomorrow," Will repeated carefully. "I shall remember that."

John Clark shrugged his shoulders. "We can't pass the word along in time. There's no way to deliver the message. I'm too old to fight, but I've tried to do my part in other ways. This time I have failed. How many men will lose their lives because of my failure I do not know."

"How much time should it take to deliver it?"

"The time it would take a man on a fast horse to get to Coleman's Inn," answered his father.

"Or a boy?" asked Will.

His father nodded. "But there's no horse."

Will's father and mother hardly noticed when

he left the room. He stopped in the kitchen only long enough to pick up two apples.

"Guns in the churchyard at Breeze Hill," muttered Will to himself as he left the house. "The British will raid tomorrow."

In the barn he took down a bridle from the wall of the harness room. Could he get it on the Red One? He'd soon know.

The big stallion was grazing near the barn. Will climbed the fence and walked toward him. The horse lifted his head.

The boy held out an apple. "Here, Red," he called. "Here's another apple."

The horse stood like a statue. The boy hardly dared to breathe. Then the Red One took a step toward him.

Will crept closer. This time the horse did not move when the apple was within his reach. He bent his head and took it readily from the boy's outstretched hand.

With one swift, sudden motion the boy slipped the bridle over the Red One's head. In a single bound he was on the horse's back.

The surprised animal quivered from mane to tail. He reared up on his hind legs. Will leaned over and patted his neck.

"Please, please!" he whispered. "We've got to do it, Red. On your way, boy. It's a straight shoot to the inn this time. I know the way now. Don't fight me, Red One. We've got to take that message to the inn!"

In some strange way the horse seemed almost to understand the boy. For a moment he hesitated. Then like a ball from a cannon he started down the road that lay before him. Will had never felt anything like this before. He knew now what real riding was—what a real horse was. Every yard of the way he felt as if he and the horse were one.

As they passed the house, Will waved to his

father and his mother, who stood openmouthed in the yard.

"I'm on my way!" he shouted to them.

Will knew he would never forget that ride even if he lived to be an old, old man. The same route had seemed exciting when York and he had delivered the horses. But it was nothing like this.

He did not attempt to hold the Red One in. He could not have done it. Nor did he want to. Straight down the trail they flew. The big horse cleared the ford at Plover's Creek in the twinkling of an eye. As they galloped around the mountain, Will rubbed his eyes to be sure that no white wings glistened in the moonlight. Surely no mortal horse could keep this speed.

He grinned at his fancy. "If you had wings I guess they'd be red. I suppose you don't, but you wouldn't surprise me if you did have them. There's not another piece of horseflesh like you in the whole world."

At last he managed to draw rein in front of the large inn in the valley. A tall, black-haired young man came out to meet him. This must be the landlord's son, Ed Coleman, Will thought. He liked the young man's frank, open face.

"Did you bring us a message?" the young man asked eagerly.

Will nodded. The Red One was dancing up and down. He was so frisky and impatient that Will could hardly control him.

"There are guns hidden in the churchyard at Breeze Hill. The British will march to seize them in the morning."

The young man whistled between his teeth. "Oh, no, they won't!" he exclaimed. "There'll be no guns by the time they arrive. We'll see to that before dawn."

Will turned the Red One in the direction of home. He was glad to be through with his part of the job.

"Climb down and have something hot to drink before you start back," Ed Coleman said. "You must be tired."

Will shook his head. He grinned down at the landlord's son. "I guess I won't, thank you. If I got off the Red One, I might never be able to mount him again."

In the Swamp

"THIS PLACE IS named right," said Randy Johnson. "Gloomy Swamp!"

Will laughed. Randy, York, and he were
tracking the old fox that had been stealing some
of the Clarks' chickens.

The boys suspected that the fox had a den on
the hill beyond the far side of Gloomy Swamp.
Tonight they were hunting for him. Their walking would have been easier if they had circled
the swamp. On the other hand, it would have
taken them an hour or so longer.

The swamp was indeed a gloomy place. Anyone who did not know it well would have been

in grave danger. Dangerous snakes hid in it —copperheads and water moccasins. The boys wore boots. At one place the water had become so deep that they had used the old boat which they kept tied up at Devil's Island. They had poled their way beneath low-hanging cypress limbs to their present location.

Suddenly Will gave an annoyed exclamation. "Thunderation! I must have left the lantern behind at Devil's Island, York. Will you take the skiff and go back for it? The moon is shining now, but if it goes behind those clouds we'll be out of luck."

"Will you wait here for me?" York asked as he climbed into the skiff.

"No, we'll go on. We're almost there now. Leave the boat here when you come back. Maybe we'll have old Mr. Fox by the time you get there with the lantern."

"Save some fun for me," York begged.

The two boys watched York disappear into the shadows with the skiff. Then they started for the edge of the swamp. Will knew the safe paths by night as well as he knew them by day. So did York. But Randy had been in the swamp only once before.

"Be careful," Will called back to him.

He leaped to a firm foothold on a near-by hummock. One misstep and he would have fallen into the dark, murky waters. In some places those waters were very deep. No one knew exactly how deep.

"We may get that fox before York gets back with the lantern," Will shouted to his companion. "I reckon we should——"

He had no time to finish his words. There was a big splash behind him. Will whirled about. Randy had lost his footing. He had fallen into the black waters.

Will started for the bank on a dead run. But

Randy was quick. He kept his head. By the time Will reached him he had grabbed a tree root twined about the base of a rotting stump. By holding to that, he pulled himself up on a solid spot of land.

Then it happened! A piece of the root slid noiselessly away into the water. In the ghostly moonlight both boys had a glimpse of two wicked eyes and a patch of white. Cruel fangs darted with lightning speed in and out of Randy's arm.

Randy's face was ashen.

Will seized him by the arm. "Come on!" he commanded. "We've got to get out of here to firmer ground."

Will dragged the terrified boy the rest of the way through the swamp. It was not far, but it seemed like miles. Several times Randy sank in a heap from fear and exhaustion. Will forced him roughly to his feet. There was no time to lose. "Come on, Randy," he urged. "I can see the edge of the swamp."

It was only a few minutes before they came out on solid ground. Randy sank down in a heap. "It was a cottonmouth—a water moccasin," he whispered. "You know what that means, Will."

"It means this," said Will in a determined voice. He drew his knife from its sheath. He did not hesitate. He felt the blade and started toward Randy.

"What are you going to do?" asked the terrified boy.

"There's just one thing to do. I must drain the poison out of your body—at once. Hold out your arm, Randy."

It was a ghostly scene. A crescent moon shone down from between dark clouds. The two boys were alone in the night on the edge of the swamp. There was no sign of York.

Will drew the blade along Randy's arm.

"Shut your eyes," he commanded. "This won't hurt—much."

His frightened companion obeyed. Will closed his jaws tight. Then he made two swift cuts a quarter-inch deep directly over the fang marks. The blood flowed freely from Randy's arm. Randy shivered.

"Keep your eyes shut," Will ordered. "The wounds must bleed awhile."

Will pulled off his shirt. Then he tore it into narrow strips. Skillfully he applied a neat bandage to Randy's outstretched arm.

Randy opened his eyes. He was still lying flat on his back. "Is it all over?" he asked fearfully.

"All but attending to Mr. Fox. Something tells me we had better save him for another night, though."

"You mean I'm not going to die?"

"Of course you are not going to die," Will promised him. "You lost a lot of blood. The poison from the snake's fangs went out with it. Your arm is swelling very little. I'll make some more cuts in about fifteen minutes just to be on the safe side."

Randy sat up and looked at his bandaged arm. "Gee! I thought I was as good as dead when that cottonmouth struck me," he said solemnly.

"You would have been dead if I hadn't seen Father doctor one of the farm hands once," Will told him.

"You saved my life," said Randy. "I don't know how to thank you."

With a wave of his hand Will disclaimed all credit. "Forget it. Anyone could have done it. But, say, let's wait for York, then take the long way home. I've had enough of that swamp for one night. We might not be so lucky next time."

The Hermit

"I REFUSE TO go to Poor Farm Hollow," said Jack Johnson.

"So do I," said Randy.

Will's blue eyes flashed fire for a minute. Then they grew quiet. He seldom lost his temper, in spite of his red hair. But he wished his friends would be sensible.

"The Hermit of Poor Farm Hollow won't hurt us," he declared. "Folks say he has a lot of Indian things—arrows, beads, wampum, and feathers, and things like that."

"He certainly won't hurt us," said Randy, "because we aren't going to the Hollow."

"That's right," Jack agreed.

Will shrugged his shoulders. "Well, then, I'm going alone."

York had been standing quietly to one side while the other boys argued. Now he stepped forward. "No, you're not," he said. "I can't say I exactly want to go, but if you go I'm coming along, too."

Will Clark slapped him on the shoulder. "Good for you, York! The others will be sorry they stayed at home."

York did not look too certain. "Wel-l-l—I hope so," he said.

A short time later Will and York were riding along the road that branched off before it reached Poor Farm Hollow. As usual, Will was riding the Red One. The boy and the horse were seldom separated during daylight hours now. York followed them on a medium-sized black horse named Caesar.

"I guess we should have told Father where we're going," Will said.

York grinned. "What will you bet that Randy and Jack are doing it right now?"

Will tapped the Red One with his heel, and the big horse broke into a long swinging gait.

"We had better hurry before we're stopped," Will called back over his shoulder.

York showed his white, even teeth in a broad smile. He would follow Will Clark anywhere.

Gradually the countryside grew rockier and hillier. For several miles the boys had passed or met no one on the road. Few people lived in Poor Farm Hollow. The soil was poor and it was difficult to make a living there.

"Why do you suppose people are so afraid of the Hermit?" York called to Will.

Will turned his head to answer. There was laughter in his voice. "They say he doesn't exactly welcome visitors."

York hesitated. "Don't you think maybe we should turn back?"

"You may turn back if you want to. I'm going to visit the Hermit."

York rode up beside his friend. "When you talk like that, I'd go through fire and water for you. Two of us are going to visit the Hermit."

"I thought you'd stay with me," said Will with a smile. "This is real adventure, York. I don't know why we didn't think of it sooner."

"I'm just as glad we didn't," York told him. "Even if you are only twelve years old, you are almost as big as a man. And I'd as soon visit the Hermit with a man as with a boy."

"Don't be foolish, York!" Will said. "There's no danger."

"No-o-o!" York agreed. "Just the same, I'm glad we each have a knife and a gun."

By now the rough trail had ended. The horses picked their way across the unfenced field.

York's black horse stumbled and almost fell. York reined him to a halt.

"I'll tell you what," Will suggested. "Let's tie the horses and walk the rest of the way."

The boys tied the Red One and Caesar to a near-by tree. Then they went the rest of the way on foot. The land grew poorer and poorer as they went along. It was not hard to see where the hollow got its name.

"How do you suppose the man keeps alive?" Will muttered. He kicked a stone from his path.

"Well, hunting is free," York said. "He probably catches a fish now and then, too."

"There's his cabin."

Will pointed to a little tumble-down cabin on the far side of a swift creek. Both boys stared. There was no sign of life. Will put his hands up to his mouth. "Hello-o-o!" he shouted.

There was no answer. Will looked at York. York looked back at him. The boys moved a step or two forward. Again Will shouted. "Hello-o-o! Anybody there?"

Still no one answered from the cabin.

"I've simply got to see what is in that cabin," Will declared. "I'm going closer, York. I don't believe anyone is inside."

The boys walked toward the cabin. Tales about the Hermit of Poor Farm Hollow were plentiful in Caroline County. He rarely visited the crossroads store. He had nothing to do with his neighbors. He was gone for weeks at a time.

"Now that we're here," Will whispered to York, "let's peep in that window."

"Raise your hands above your head and turn around," ordered a gruff voice behind them.

The boys obeyed. They looked into the barrel of a long rifle. It was in the hands of a tall man with a long gray beard.

"Raise them higher," he commanded.

Will looked at York. This was no laughing

matter. The Hermit meant business. He looked rather wild.

"What are you doing here?" he asked sternly.

The boys were too frightened to speak. At last Will found his voice. "We came to see your— your Indian collection," he faltered.

"How did you know I have an Indian collection?" the man asked.

"Everybody knows that," Will said boldly. "People have talked about it ever since you came here to live."

"A man can have no secrets," the Hermit said with a sigh.

"Why don't you want people to know about your things?" Will asked.

"Maybe I like to be alone," said the man. "Maybe I like to remember the things I saw beyond the mountains—the great rivers, the forests, the lakes, the grassy plains, the great herds of buffaloes."

He took a step forward. The boys saw that he walked with a bad limp.

"That's too bad——" York began.

But Will's eyes were shining. "You have been to those places? Where I want to go?"

The man was smiling now. "Where do you want to go, young man?"

"West!" exclaimed Will.

The man laid down his gun. He did not look at all wild now. His face was kind and friendly. "As one explorer to another—will you come into my cabin?"

He swung wide the heavy door and beckoned to the boys. They needed no second invitation. Their eyes grew wide with astonishment.

The walls were lined with trophies. A stuffed grouse stood on the mantel. But the wonder of wonders was a slender birchbark canoe that filled the whole center of the room. It was hung from the overhead beams by ropes.

Will ran his hands along its smooth sides. He gave a little whistle of delight.

"If you had seen half that canoe has seen, you'd be a real traveler," his host told him.

"When Will starts exploring, he's going to take me with him," York told their new friend.

"I hope you'll both be good pathfinders," the man said. "Sit down, boys. I'll tell you about some of the places that canoe has been."

"To Kentucky?" Will asked.

The Hermit laughed. "That was only the beginning," he said.

"My brother is in Kentucky," said Will.

"Who is your brother?" the man asked.

"George Rogers Clark, sir."

"General Clark? Why, lad, he's the greatest man in the Western lands today. America can thank him for the vast Northwest."

"You know him?" Will asked eagerly.

"Yes," said the man. "I've talked with him and

eaten with him—and I wish I had marched with him. I would have, too, but I was down in the Wautauga Country when he set off for Kaskaskia and Vincennes. Besides, I had this bad leg even then and wouldn't have been of much help to him, I suppose."

"To think you have been living here for two years and we didn't know about you!" exclaimed Will. "You must come with me to see my father and my mother. Anyone who knows George is welcome at our house."

"I'd be proud to meet the parents of General Clark," the man said.

"Why do you hide away in this old cabin?" Will asked. "Many people around here are interested in the West. They would like to hear you talk about it."

The man looked down at his worn, tattered clothes. "Maybe it's pride," he said at last. "I can't do much hard work any more. Back here in Poor Farm Hollow I can keep alive by hunting and fishing. I guess I must seem a little crazy to folks who don't know me. I've heard that I do anyhow. But I don't have to ask for charity back here."

"Well, that's all over," said Will simply. "You must come home with me. I know my father will find something you can do—either on the farm or at Fredericksburg."

Captured by Indians

I⊤ was October, 1783. The tall thirteen-year-old boy in buckskins had climbed the little mountain near Charlottesville where Mr. Jefferson had built his house.

The house and the view were beautiful as he had imagined. He strode up the slope and ran up the steps of the east veranda. He pulled the bell at the door of the mansion.

Presently a tall, dignified Negro opened the great front door.

"Is Mr. Jefferson at home?" Will asked.

The man shook his head. "Mr. Jefferson has gone to Philadelphia to attend Congress."

Will was disappointed. He had hoped to meet the family friend of whom he had heard so much.

"Is there anything I can do?" The servant asked politely.

"No-o-o, I guess not," Will said. "I'm going up into the Shenandoah Mountains for a few days. I thought I'd like to talk with Mr. Jefferson before I went."

A smile crossed the man's face. "He'll be sorry he missed you. Before the war, whenever he had the time, he would ramble through the hills every week or so."

Will was starting down the veranda steps. He turned to look back. "Please tell him Mr. Clark's son was here."

The man took a step forward. "Mr. John Clark who moved to Caroline County?"

Will nodded. "He's my father."

The Negro opened the door of Monticello wide. "Won't you come in? Mr. Jefferson would never forgive me if I allowed Mr. Clark's son to leave without inviting him in. I'm his man Martin," he added.

Will gladly turned and made his way into the house. He stared about him in the broad entrance hall. Above him a little balcony opened on upstairs bedrooms. On the first floor he caught a glimpse of wide doors and a dining room beyond.

Martin caught the gleam of interest in the boy's eyes. "Mr. Jefferson himself designed the house," he explained. "It's unlike other Virginian houses. Would you care to see his bedroom and private sitting room?"

He took Will about the house and grounds. The boy watched eagerly as his guide showed him the master's recessed bed. Martin demonstrated how it could be drawn up into the ceiling to make more space in the little sitting room. He noticed the narrow walled-in stairs leading to the second floor. They were designed, Martin told him, to allow little heat to escape upward. Every inch of space in the house was used. Yet Mr. Jefferson, Will knew, had never studied architecture in any college.

The boy thought his tour had ended. But he was mistaken.

"If you're going up into the mountains to explore, perhaps you'd be interested in some of Mr. Jefferson's collections," Martin said.

He led the way to a room at the rear of the house near the servants' quarters. There box after box was piled all the way to the ceiling.

Martin put his hand into an open box and drew out a stuffed snake. Will had never seen one exactly like it.

"This came from a Frenchman who traveled in the West," Martin told him. "Mr. Jefferson is constantly writing letters and receiving them about the Western lands."

"The West," Will repeated thoughtfully. "I may be going to Kentucky before long."

Martin smiled. "Mr. Jefferson didn't stop with Kentucky. He's interested in more than that. Many times I've seen him stand for an hour staring across the mountains. He was always talking about what lies beyond the Mississippi."

For a long while Will sat poring over the contents of a very large unsealed box. There were stuffed beavers and otters, a savage wolf larger than any the boy had ever seen, and a sly little red fox. There were pressed plants labeled with strange Latin names. There were unusual Indian trophies. He wished that he could talk with Mr. Jefferson about them.

At last Will turned his back on Monticello and went on his way into the mountains.

He did not go very far that day. Before long he pitched camp beside a noisy little rivulet that came rippling down out of the hills. Beside the campfire in the dusk he broiled a rabbit he had shot. That night he slept beneath the stars.

SURPRISE FOR WILL

Early next morning he went on his way. He was eager to reach the skyline and look over into the western world beyond. He saw no sign of human life on the way up. He had been told that there were a few friendly Indians in these parts, but he did not see them.

Higher and higher he climbed. Earlier in the day it had been quite warm. But at this height it was cool.

He stopped and stared down into the valley below. He could see the roofs of a few cabins here and there.

He propped a foot on a fallen log and leaned forward for a better view. Suddenly something whizzed past his head.

He could hardly believe his eyes! An arrow quivered directly in front of him in the trunk of a tree. Friendly Indians, indeed!

He turned hastily about. Not ten feet away stood an Indian boy several inches taller than he.

96

His copper-colored skin glistened in the sunlight. He had a long wicked-looking knife in his hand.

Taken by surprise, Will was helpless. His hand stole toward the hunting knife at his belt. The Indian took a threatening step forward.

He made a sign for Will to walk in front of him. Will obeyed unwillingly. Presently they came to a narrow trail that led back into the woods. It was choked by briers and undergrowth. The Indian youth did not slacken his pace. With that gleaming knife at his back Will continued to walk fast.

The Indian did not say a word. Once in a while he made a sound to show a turn. Will tried several times to talk with him, but without success. Finally he gave up.

For nearly two hours they pushed on. Will could tell that their path went steadily upward. But he was completely lost. He had no idea where he was being taken. Perhaps when night came he could escape from his captor.

At length the two came out on a little clearing. Beside a small campfire sat an old, old Indian wrapped in a blanket. He stood up as Will and the young Indian drew near. His face was dark and stern. "What does this mean?" he asked in perfect English.

Will sighed with relief. Here at last was someone with whom he could talk, friendly or not. "You'll have to ask him," he said. He pointed to the boy behind him.

"What does this mean?" the old man repeated to the Indian youth.

"He was too near our trail," the boy said sullenly, without looking up.

"Did he do you any harm?" the old man asked.

The Indian boy shook his head.

"Then by what right did you bring him here? Our people, the few who are left, have lived in these mountains in peace with the settlers below us for a hundred years. We have left them the valleys. Those who cross these mountains to the Western lands seldom see us. We can live for generations longer in this country of our forefathers. Let others of our race make war. We shall live and die in peace."

The young Indian stood with his head down. Will began to feel sorry for him.

"Don't be too hard on him," he told the old Indian. "He scared me half to death when he came upon me all of a sudden and let that arrow fly. But it's all right now that I know he didn't really want to harm me. But say, this seems like a dream! I knew there were friendly Indians in these mountains, but I didn't know they spoke English so well."

The old man smiled. "Only a small number of my tribe are left. Long ago we decided to stay here instead of pushing westward. We live as Indians in these free hills, but we find it well to speak the language of the white man."

Will could hardly believe his ears. "I wish there were more Indians like you."

The old Indian gave a grunt of approval. "I wish there were more white men like you! Many of them are bad. They drink, steal, lie, and kill!"

"Why, that is just what my people say about the Indians!" said Will in surprise.

The Indian grunted. "Perhaps they are both right sometimes."

"I'm learning things today," Will said. "When I'm a man, I'd like to help white men and Indians understand each other."

"Why are you here?" the old Indian asked. "What brings you up on the ridge?"

Will drew a deep breath. "It's a long story. Let's just put it this way. Someday I'm going west. I thought I'd like to climb as high as I could and look over into what lies beyond."

The old Indian nodded. "My grandson and I will take you to the top of the ridge."

The Indian youth had sheathed his knife by this time. He looked like the Red One, Will thought, standing there handsome and wild and free. The Indian boy's grandfather motioned for him to lead the way.

It was a long climb. This time, however, Will enjoyed every step of the way. There was no threatening knife at his back. Still he could hardly believe that he, Will Clark from Caroline County, was climbing to the Allegheny skyline in the company of two friendly, English-speaking Indians.

Gradual as the climb was, Will felt his head pounding and his breath short. The Indians showed no signs of discomfort. At last they came out on a grassy stretch that overlooked the valley to the west.

Far down below lay the land. Beyond the

great valley was a ridge of mountains. Beyond that ridge was another, and another, and another. Altogether Will counted seven ridges before the blue line of the mountains faded away into the distant sky.

He turned to his old guide. "Isn't there room over yonder for both white and red people?"

The old man shook his head. "I doubt it, my son. There has been too much blood spilled between them. Wrongs have been done on each side. Someday there may be peace. As for me, I have dwelt in peace these many years. I shall do so until the Great Spirit calls me."

A sense of awe crept over Will. He felt as though he had become a man and had left boyhood behind. He held out his hand to the Indian youth. He forgot that it was a white man's gesture. The boy took his hand as though he did not know what to do with it.

"I'm not afraid to fight when I have to," Will

102

told him. "But I'd rather have you for a friend than an enemy."

"Nor am I," the boy replied proudly. "But friends it shall be."

Will turned away from the Indians. He forgot he was not alone. He stared over the distant blue hills.

"So that is Kentucky yonder," he said to himself. "That is My Promised Land. When shall I go there?"

A Letter and a Map

"THERE IT IS," said General Clark, who was home on a visit. He handed a letter to his youngest brother, Will.

Thirteen-year-old Will's hand shook slightly as he took it from George. His eyes followed the closely written lines. They were penned by the hand of the man who had written the Declaration of Independence. This same man was a friend of George and his father. Will hoped that he would someday be a friend of his.

He read the message. It was written from Annapolis, Maryland. Congress was meeting in Annapolis, Will knew.

Dec. 4, 1783

Dear Sir,

I find they have subscribed a very large sum in England for exploring the country from the Mississippi to California. They pretend it is only to promote knowledge. I am afraid they have thought of colonizing into that quarter. Some of us have been talking here in a feeble way of making an attempt to search that country, but I doubt whether we have enough of that kind of spirit to raise the money. How would you like to lead such a party? Though I am afraid our prospect is not worth the question.

THOS. JEFFERSON

Your friend and humble servant,

"There it is," said George again. "At least *he* believes in me."

Will felt very sorry for George. The hardships of the Northwest campaign had made an old man of him. Besides, he had used all his money and as much credit as he could raise to outfit his men. He had expected to be repaid. But instead of money Virginia had given him a beautful sword and a letter of thanks. That was all. Now George Rogers Clark was a poor man. He was heavily in debt and in danger of losing his property.

But Will forgot all this as he read the letter. "In plain words, what does Mr. Jefferson mean, George?" he asked.

"He means that England has not given up hope of owning a part of the New World," George said slowly. "If we do not claim the vast lands west of the Mississippi, England will."

"And he wants you to explore the land," Will whispered. "Say you will go and take me with you, George."

"I am an old man, Will," said General Clark sadly. "Too old for that."

"Why, George, you're only thirty-one!" Will exclaimed in surprise.

"True enough," George said. "But the hardships of my campaign aged me so that I would be no good as an explorer."

106

Will could not answer at once. He knew that George was right. At last he spoke. "Mr. Jefferson will send someone, won't he?"

George shook his head. "I doubt it. The words in that letter are the words of a dreamer, Will. He lacks money and authority. Dreamers get nowhere."

"What is it like beyond the Mississippi?" Will asked. "Have you been there?"

General Clark shook his head. "Who knows, lad? Only brave men would venture up the Missouri River from St. Louis. There will be danger and heartbreak between St. Louis and the Pacific Ocean."

"I want to go there more than I want to do anything else in the whole world," Will said.

"Maybe you will someday. But I am worn out. It is too late for me. And you had better forget it. As I said, dreamers don't get anywhere."

Will Clark stood up tall and straight. His blue

eyes flashed. Big-boned and broad-shouldered, he looked more like a man than a boy of thirteen. "It may be only a dream, but it's my dream. Someday I'm going west. I've simply got to, George. Don't you understand?"

General Clark smiled at the boy. "I hope you will if you really want to that much. In the meantime, here's something more practical. I'm moving the family to Kentucky next year."

"Kentucky at last!"

For a short time Will had forgotten about Kentucky. Now here was a part of his boyhood dream coming true. For years he had hoped for it. Before too long the whole family would be on their way.

He gave a happy shout. He took to his heels. General Clark called after him. "Where are you going, Will?"

Will stopped only a moment at the door. "I'm going to tell York to begin packing!"

"Here is Stony Cave, and here is home." Will Clark was lying on his stomach before the fire. He drew a firm straight line on the sheet of paper with a stubby bit of charcoal.

He rolled over and sat up to take a better look at his work. His companion, Meriwether Lewis, looked at the sketch with interest.

Although Will was the older by four years, the two boys were fast friends. Will had rescued the younger boy from drowning in a cave nearly two years ago. Since then they had spent much time together.

Now they were at the home of Meriwether's uncle, Mr. Fielding Lewis, in Fredericksburg. He and his wife, who was a sister of General Washington, always made the boys welcome.

Will had come to Fredericksburg on business for his father. He had permission to stay several days with the Lewises. It was to be his last visit with "Merne" Lewis before the Clarks started for Kentucky.

He stood up and laid aside the drawing. "That's enough for today," he said, yawning. "Let's go shopping, Merne. I'd like to find something for my father's birthday."

Meriwether agreed gladly. He always wanted to do whatever Will suggested. Even a stroll through the shops of the town was an adventure when Will was along.

Presently the two boys were walking along the main street of Fredericksburg. They passed the Rising Sun Tavern and stopped a little farther down the street to look in the window of a small bookshop.

"I don't care much for books," Will said. "Besides, I don't think a shilling will buy a very good book." He looked down at the coin in his hand.

Meriwether said, "Maybe he doesn't want a book, anyhow."

Will's face brightened. "No, I don't believe he does. He's too busy on the plantation to read very much."

The boys stopped next at Hensley's stationery shop. Will opened the door and entered. A little bell tinkled overhead. Meriwether followed him through the door.

"Good morning, boys," said the owner. "What can I do for you this fine morning?"

Will stepped forward. His blue eyes shone. His hair looked redder than usual. "I'd like to buy a birthday present for my father."

Mr. Hensley rubbed his hands together. "Now let me see," he began. "How about a nice box for his desk? Here's a nice one. It came over from England before the war." He held up a small brass box with a hinged top.

"How much is it?" Will asked hopefully.

"Only two shillings."

Will shook his head. He had only one shilling.

The owner of the shop looked along his shelves. "Here's the very thing for a gentleman. It's a fine snuffbox."

"How much?" said Will again.

"You may have it for a shilling and a sixpence," replied Mr. Hensley.

Will shook his head sadly. He had not known that shops charged such prices.

"How much money do you have?" Mr. Hensley was getting a little impatient.

Will swallowed hard. "Only one shilling."

The shop owner frowned slightly. "I fear I have nothing in my shop for so small a sum. The war has made prices high."

"Aunt Betty will let you have some money, Will," said Meriwether.

Will shook his head. "Father always tells me never to borrow. Besides, how could I ever pay it back? We don't have much money at our house except when the tobacco is sold. We don't need it. When we want anything a neighbor has, we trade him something for it."

The boys were about to leave when Will had an idea. He turned to his friend. "I could draw him a picture, Merne."

"So you could," Meriwether agreed eagerly. "Better still, Will, why don't you draw him a map? He'd like that."

"A map?" Will looked hard at Meriwether. He had not thought of that. It seemed a good suggestion. "Well——" he began.

Then a brand-new idea came to him. His blue eyes danced. He turned back to Mr. Hensley. "Do you have a piece of heavy white paper, sir?" he asked eagerly.

"The very best white parchment," Mr. Hensley assured him. He reached carefully behind the counter and pulled out a large box. From it he took carefully a large sheet of fine, creamy white paper. "Is this what you want?"

Will nodded eagerly. "And some ink, too, please," he added.

Mr. Hensley placed a small black bottle beside the parchment paper. "My very best India ink. You may have it and the paper for a shilling."

Happily Will laid his money on the counter. He felt sure this present would please his father. He had always praised his son's drawings.

Meriwether and he raced down the steps of the little shop. Will carried the precious paper in a roll under his arm. "I'm going to draw a map," he announced proudly.

"What map do you intend to draw?" Meriwether asked as they walked along.

Will stopped still. He had not thought of that. "A map of Caroline County, I guess. I know it best of any place."

"That will be nice," Meriwether agreed.

Suddenly Will slapped his friend on the back. "I have a still better idea, Merne. I'll make a map that shows the two routes to Kentucky, the one through Cumberland Gap and the one down the Ohio River."

The two boys rushed into the Lewis house.

"Mrs. Lewis!" shouted Will.

"Aunt Betty!" called Meriwether.

Mrs. Lewis appeared in the door of the dining room. "Mercy on us!" she exclaimed. "I thought something was wrong. What do you boys want?"

Will thought she looked very much like her brother, General Washington, as she stood there. Will had seen him only once. He had looked stern then. But Mrs. Lewis began to laugh at the excited boys.

"May we look at the map in Uncle Fielding's study?" asked Meriwether.

"I'm going to draw a map for my father's birthday present," Will told her.

"That is thoughtful of you, Will," she said. "Of course you may look at the maps."

In a short time the boys found a map that showed the water route to Kentucky. Another map showed the route by land through Cumberland Gap. Will began to make a rough sketch of his map on brown paper. He wanted his work to be as perfect as possible before he used the store paper.

"It's too bad you haven't any paints," said Meriwether. "The map would be prettier if you painted it."

"Who says I haven't paints?" Will demanded. "Haven't you ever heard of pokeberry ink and walnut dye? I can make them myself. Just wait until my map is finished, Merne!"

"How did you happen to think of those things, Will?" asked Merriwether.

Will laughed. "You don't have to buy everything in a store," he said. "You just look about you and use your head." He went on with his slow, careful drawing.

Meriwether looked over his shoulder. "You know, Will, I think you're just about the best mapmaker in the whole world," he declared at last. "Someday you and I will go exploring together. When we do, you will make maps that will show people what the country we explore is like."

Off to Kentucky

THE DAY HAD come at last. Young Will Clark, fourteen years old and tall as any man, sat astride the Red One. He looked up and down the little line of three wagons, two cows, and several pack horses. The Clarks were about to leave Virginia forever.

Will rode back to the rear wagon. York was the driver. His passengers were Old York and Rose. They were his father and mother. All their household goods were in the wagon.

"Are you ready, York?" Will asked.

York nodded. "The sooner the better!"

Will rode forward to the first wagon. His

brother Jonathan was driving it. Richard and Edmund sat beside him. All the girls except Fanny were with Jonathan and Richard. She was in the second wagon with their parents.

Will cracked his whip. The wagons began to roll. From his saddle Will turned to look back at the house on the hill. Then he rode to the front of the little procession.

They were off to Kentucky!

Nothing happened the first day. The road was rough, but it was still passable. Travelers could use it until the winter rains set in.

Will was happy when he sat beside the camp-fire that night. The stars were shining. Although it was late October, 1784, the weather was warm. Will felt comfortable and well fed. Mother, the girls, and Rose had prepared a delicious supper.

"We should come to Braddock's Road by the day after tomorrow," said Mr. Clark. "The British general made it twenty years ago when he fought the French and the Indians. Now we too will travel the road to Pittsburgh. We must travel fast, though. George will be anxious until we arrive in Louisville."

The Clarks did not travel so fast as they had expected. First an axle broke. Then the door of a chicken coop flew open. Four hens ran squawking into the woods. The younger Clark girls with Will and York ran laughing after them. It was more than an hour before the fowl were safe in their coop again.

As the third night approached, they were still twenty miles from Braddock's Road. A cold drizzling rain was falling.

Will's father called to him, "We had better get under cover. I saw a little tavern about a mile behind us. I think we'll turn back. We'll spend the night there."

The boy agreed unwillingly. He hated to lose the time. They must start their journey down the Ohio soon if they did not want to become icebound at Pittsburgh.

The drivers turned their horses back. By now the air was chill. The women and the girls huddled together for warmth. The men walked to make the loads lighter. They tried to urge the weary horses along.

Finally they came to the inn. It was a tumble-down affair. There was a pine-knot flare stuck in the ground outside the door. Will said nothing. He thought, however, that he would rather spend the night in the rain than inside that place. It looked anything but inviting.

It was no better on the inside. The general room was bare and dirty. The Clarks seemed to be the only guests. The landlord came to meet them. He had a sullen face. He wore a black patch over one eye. Will felt uneasy.

He felt no better when his father drew out a little bag of goldpieces. The landlord licked his lips greedily. He could hardly take his eyes off the little leather bag.

DESPERATE MEN

The Clarks were gathered about the rough pine table in the center of the room. The landlord brought them steaming stew. It was hot and well flavored. Will tried to forget his fears.

"We must get to bed early," Mr. Clark said. "We may not reach Braddock's Road even tomorrow."

John Clark rose from the table. He felt his belt where the bag of gold pieces was fastened. Will saw the landlord's eyes on his father.

The inn grew dark and quiet. Mrs. Clark and the girls were all sleeping in one room. Mr. Clark and three of his sons were in another. Because the men's bedroom was crowded, the landlord had placed a straw pallet for Will at the far end of the upper hall under the eaves. When all the others had gone to bed, Will lay down on the pallet and covered himself with a blanket.

He could hear the regular breathing of different members of his family. Everyone was asleep—everyone but Will. For some reason he was wide awake.

Suddenly he heard a noise downstairs. He raised his head from the pillow. There was a creak of boards below. Will stole to the head of the stairs.

Two men were seated at the long table. They were the landlord and a stranger. Will could not see their faces. The stranger was wrapped in a black cloak. He had a three-cornered hat pulled down over his eyes. He looked like a highwayman.

The landlord glanced upstairs. Will shrank into the shadows.

"Get rid of the sons first. Then the old man

will be no trouble," the landlord whispered. "I'll take care of the woman and the girls."

"What about the boy?"

The landlord gave a shrug. "We can handle him easily enough."

Will shuddered in his corner. He had known there was something evil about this house.

He crept back along the narrow hall toward his pallet. He would get his pistol from under his pillow. Then he would rouse his brothers.

But he was not so quick as the robbers. A door banged below. There was the sound of heavy footsteps, too.

"Is there a man by the name of Jonathan Clark here?" a gruff voice demanded.

The words had wakened Jonathan. He stumbled to the door of the bedroom. His eyes were heavy with sleep. "Who wants me?" he asked.

Will tried to get to his brother. But the man below had stepped to the foot of the stairs. Will knew he must have a drawn pistol beneath that dark cloak. The boy could not cross the hall without being seen.

"Are you Jonathan Clark?" the man below demanded. He sounded excited.

"I am," answered Jonathan sleepily.

"Thank heaven I've found you! There's a wounded man lying in a ditch down the road. I wanted to bring him here, but he wouldn't let me touch him. He asked me to find you. I fear he's dying."

Will tried to call to his brother. The words stuck in his throat. He knew the landlord and the stranger must be heavily armed. At the moment Jonathan was not.

By this time old John Clark was standing in the door of his bedroom. "Hurry, boys!" he urged. "You must hurry!"

The Clark brothers went racing down the steps. Will hesitated no longer. He ran back to the pallet. He snatched up the pistol that lay under the pillow. Escape by way of the first floor was cut off!

Will climbed out the back window of his brothers' bedroom. He caught at a near-by limb

and swung down the tree to the ground. He must stop his brothers before it was too late!

But he was already too late. He ran around a corner of the inn just as they galloped off into the night.

Will's heart rose in his mouth. Now only he and his father were left. He cocked his pistol, then stole back through the low back door and looked about him. The men were upstairs now. Will could hear their voices.

"Help!" John Clark called. "Jonathan! Edmund! Richard! Help!"

"Yell on, old man," a voice sneered from the upper hall. "They won't hear you."

"Don't take my money," Mr. Clark begged. "We need it to use in Kentucky."

"Stay in Virginia," another voice mocked. "Kentucky is a dangerous place."

Will ran back under the stairs. His pistol was primed and ready.

"Tie the old man up tight," the landlord advised. "I attended to the girls and the old woman. Their door is locked."

Will was hot with rage. He could hear the two men coming down the stairs. Soon the highwayman would escape with the money. No doubt he would return later to share it with the landlord. Will could hear muffled groans coming from above.

The footsteps came on. As the two men reached the first floor, Will stepped out from his hiding place. He aimed the pistol straight toward them. "Raise your arms high. Drop that bag of money," he ordered.

The men hesitated. He had taken them by surprise. The landlord dropped the little leather bag. The highwayman took a step toward it.

"I'll shoot to kill," Will warned him. "I intend to protect my parents and my sisters. I advise you not to try to escape. Sit down."

Unwillingly the robber and the landlord obeyed him. Will did not take his eyes from them for a single instant. He kept the barrel of his pistol pointed at them. His arm grew tired and began to ache, but he stood his ground.

At last he heard his brothers returning. They stamped up to the door of the inn.

"What a pack of foolishness this was!" Jonathon growled angrily.

"There was no man anywhere—hurt or well," Edmund added.

"A wild-goose chase——" began Richard.

Then they entered the room. Their eyes grew wide when they saw Will holding his pistol on the two captive men.

Will did not move a muscle. "Draw your guns, boys," he said. "My arm is getting tired."

The robbers made a dash for the rear door. Will fired and missed. His brothers ran after the escaping men, but they were too late. By

130

the time they reached the door the two men were riding away on horseback into the night.

Will laid down his smoking pistol. He started toward the stairs. "Our visitors are gone," he shouted up to his parents. "I'm coming up to free you. We'll have the place all to ourselves for the rest of the night."

A Boat Is Built

"Do we start building the boat today?" Will
asked. He was standing in the door of the Clark
cabin at Pittsburgh. He and his family were
waiting there to begin their journey down the
Ohio River to Kentucky.

His brother Jonathan nodded. "We may already be too late. If the river freezes over we
must stay here until spring. George will be anxious if we do not reach the settlement at the Falls
of the Ohio before Christmas."

A few minutes later Will with his older
brother was riding briskly down the streets of
the busy frontier town. Will was on the Red

132

One, and Jonathan rode a big bay horse. They passed ladies and gentlemen in silks and satins. They saw tradesmen and rivermen.

At last Will and his brother rode up to a long low shed near the bank of the river. Will could hear the z-z-z-z of a saw.

Will dismounted and tied the Red One to a hitching post. Jonathan put his horse beside the Red One. Then the two Clarks entered the shed.

Inside the low room a sawyer and his son were working on a half-finished boat. They laid down their tool as Will and Jonathan came up.

"That looks like fun," Will said.

The man smiled. "It's not so easy as it looks."

"I want to talk with you about making us a flatboat to go to Kentucky," said Jonathan.

"I'm your man," the sawyer replied. "Isaac Young is my name."

Mr. Young's son looked out the door at the horses. Jonathan's bay was standing quietly.

The Red One was pawing the ground impatiently. "You'll never get that big red horse on a flatboat," he declared. "And if you do, you'll never keep him on it. He'll leap right over the side long before you reach Kentucky."

Will's heart sank. He knew the boy was right.

"We'll need a big boat. We have a large family," Jonathan was saying.

"Fourteen persons," Will added. "All of us and York's family, too."

Jonathan frowned. "We must watch expenses," he said.

"You'll need a boat about forty feet long," the man figured. "I charge a dollar and a quarter a foot. That will be fifty dollars."

"That's a lot of money," Jonathan said slowly.

Will touched his brother on the arm. "Couldn't I help build it? That would make it cheaper."

Mr. Young looked hard at the tall boy. "Can you handle a hammer and a saw?"

Will gave a little laugh. "I think I can drive a nail without hitting my thumb."

"He's a good carpenter," Jonathan said. "How many boats have you built by now, Will?"

Will smiled. "I've built at least one every year for the last four years."

The sawyer's eyes twinkled. "If you can drive a nail and use a saw, you may help me. Yes, I will lower my price."

"That's a bargain!" said Will eagerly.

WILL MAKES A TRADE

Every day Will rode over to work on the flatboat. Mr. Young and Tom were pleasant companions. Will allowed Tom to ride the Red One now and then. Next to Meriwether Lewis, Will like Tom Young better than any boy he had ever known.

The boat was built in the workhouse a few

yards from the broad river. Each day the craft showed a big change. Sometimes Mr. Young worked with the boys. Often he allowed them to work alone. At times York helped, too. Finally the boat was almost finished.

Will laid down his hammer and stepped back to look at it. "Isn't she a beauty?" he said. "She's strong and sturdy. Not even the currents and shoals of the Ohio will weaken her. There's plenty of room for all the Clarks, and York's family, too."

"But not for the Red One," said Tom Young. "I believe that horse would go mad on the narrow deck of a flatboat."

Both boys looked over at a near-by field. The Red One, his head held high, was galloping toward the boys. He looked wild and free. Will went over to the Red One and led him back to where Tom sat.

Will felt a lump in his throat. "I know you're

right, Tom," he said gruffly. "What am I going to do about that horse?"

"You'll have to leave him behind, I guess," Tom said.

A sudden idea came to Will. It hurt him to think of parting with the Red One. And yet he might have to give him up, whether he wanted to or not. "Do you suppose your father would accept him as part payment on the boat?" he asked Tom slowly. "He's a fine horse."

"I know he will," said Tom eagerly. "I've heard him say he admired the Red One."

Will was thinking aloud now. "We Clarks haven't much money. George owns a lot of land, but land is cheap. It won't pay big debts like this. And Father has big debts, too."

"Will you trade the Red One to Father and me?" Tom urged.

It was hard for Will to agree. His voice was husky. "You will be good to him?"

138

"You know I will. I'm almost as fond of that horse as you are, Will Clark."

"I don't want to give him up. It's the hardest thing I have ever done. But I know I must. He can't be cooped up on a flatboat. And it will help Father and George. If I have to let him go, I'd rather you had him than almost anyone I know. Yes, I'll do it, Tom."

Down the Ohio

"WE'RE ON OUR way at last, York!" said Will. The boys were standing at the front of the flat-boat. The rest of the family were in the low cabin that covered the greater part of the square deck. Jonathan and Edmund Clark were in the stern fifty feet away. They were guiding the big boat out into the channel where the current was swiftest.

"Good-by, Pittsburgh!" called York.

"Hello, Kentucky!" Will grinned.

"Aren't we traveling north?" York asked in a puzzled tone.

"If you have ever looked at a map, you must

140

have seen that the river loops northward before it turns southwest."

"You know just about everything, don't you?" York asked with respect.

Will laughed. "No, not quite, York. But I want to be an explorer, and an explorer must know something about directions."

York shrugged his shoulders. "Don't forget I'm coming along. I'll let you attend to directions, Will."

Will walked to the edge of the boat. He looked down into the rushing icy waters. They lay not more than five feet below him.

"My, how we're speeding! We must be going more than ten miles an hour. The winter freeze held us up. But the spring flood will carry us down to Kentucky in nearly half the time. I'll bet George looks for us at the wharf every day."

York glanced toward the stern of the boat where Jonathan was steering the big boat out into the middle of the river. "I'm glad Mr. Jonathan is our pilot."

Will's face brightened. "He's promised to let me steer the boat now and then. He says if I helped build it, I may help navigate it."

At the end of the third day the Clarks anchored at Point Pleasant. Will listened eagerly as his father told him and his sisters the story of the battle fought there eleven years before. It was fought between men from Virginia and Indians. The white men had won, but there was great loss of life on each side.

Another flatboat had tied up near the Clark boat. While Will was listening wide-eyed in the warm, cozy cabin to tales of war there came a knock at the door.

Will sprang to open it. Outside on the windy deck stood another boy. "My mother sent me over to ask you for a bit of yeast dough," he said. "Something has happened to hers."

Ann Clark hurried to wrap a piece of light snowy dough in a piece of cloth. She was proud of her feathery bread. She liked to share it. "Tell your mother I'll be over to see her in the morning unless you're leaving early," she told the boy.

The boy shook his head. "We're lying over tomorrow. My father wants to hunt. He thinks he can bring down a few ducks and maybe get some squirrels and rabbits."

"Why don't we all do that?" Will asked.

The boy looked disappointed. "I thought you might like to go along with me to see the battlefield. My father has been telling me about the big fight."

"Why, that's just what my father has been doing," said Will. "I'd like to go with you."

Mr. Clark nodded. "Take a holiday tomorrow, Will. The other boys and I will shoot all the game we need."

The next morning dawned cold and clear.

After breakfast Will went out on deck. He leaped over the side of the boat. He ran out on the firm thick ice that lay between him and shore. The Clarks had not been able to tie up to land. They had pulled in as close as they could. Then they had dropped anchor.

The boy who had borrowed the dough was waiting on shore for him. "Hello, Will," he called with a friendly grin.

"Hello," Will replied. "I forgot to ask your name last night."

"It's Carl Long," the boy answered.

"Let's get started," Will suggested.

"We won't have to come back at noon if we don't want to," Carl told Will. "I brought some food." He showed Will a deerskin pouch strapped to his belt. "Mother fixed it for us."

Will liked this boy. There was something about him that reminded him of Merne Lewis back in Virginia.

144

In another moment he and Carl were running like two young deer across the vast meadow. Once Indians and white men had fought here in mortal combat. The boys could almost imagine that the battle was still going on.

"This must be where the Indians came whooping out of ambush to surround General Lewis," said Will.

They stopped to stare about them. "And along there must be where Colonel Isaac Shelby made a rear attack," Carl added.

Will and Carl both knew the story well. The battle was fresh in every Virginian's mind. Every father told it to his son.

Will wandered up and down the battlefield. He wished with all his heart that Meriwether were along. Then he turned to speak with Carl.

But Carl was far away. Will could see him at the edge of the Kanawha River. The younger boy was venturing out on the ice. Will decided he must have lived in a town to know so little of his danger.

He cupped his hands to his mouth. "Don't go any farther. The ice gets thinner!"

Perhaps Carl did not hear him. Perhaps he did not want to. Will watched uneasily as the boy put more distance between him and the shore. The temperature was low, but there was a hint of spring in the air. Will did not trust that ice. He wished he had kept an eye on the younger boy.

Suddenly there was a frightened cry. Before Will's horrified eyes Carl disappeared into the depths of the river. The ice had broken!

His head bobbed up above the surface. He tried to climb out on the ice, but fell back. Will knew what had happened. The ice had again broken under his weight.

"Tread water!" Will shouted. "I'm coming!"

He looked about him. The flatboats were over

a hill out of sight. They were too far away. There was no time to get help from there.

Then he saw almost at his feet a weather-beaten piece of timber with an iron ring in the end of it. It lay half buried in the hard ground.

Will knew what it was as soon as he saw it. Long ago on the day of the battle it had been part of an oxcart. It was the tongue that fastened the oxen to the cart.

Will dropped down on his hands and knees. He dug frantically. His hands were raw and bleeding from clawing at the frozen ground. Now the piece of timber was almost loose. He hardly felt the pain in his bleeding hands. He must pry that wagon tongue up!

Another moment passed. Then he was half dragging, half carrying the piece of timber across the meadow. He could still see the top of Carl's dark head.

"Hold on!" he shouted.

He ran out on the ice for a short distance. Then he pushed the tongue along in front of him. He lay flat on his stomach and began to wriggle forward. He pushed the timber ahead of him slowly.

Slowly it reached the hole in the ice. Will was not far behind it. He did not dare stand up. The ice would crack more if he put his entire weight in one spot. He pushed the tongue a little farther.

"Grab it!"

Carl stretched out his arms. He was so weak from cold and fright that his fingers refused to close over it. "I c-can't!" he moaned.

"Try harder!" Will urged.

Again Carl stretched out his arms and tried to grasp the wood. Again his frozen fingers were too weak.

There was only one way. Will took it.

He inched forward over the wagon tongue.

His body touched the ice on either side. But his weight was divided over several square feet. At last he got to the hole in the ice.

He reached out for Carl. The boy had little strength left. He clung feebly to Will's outstretched hands.

Will hardly dared to breathe. Could he get Carl out before the ice cracked and broke again?

He held the younger boy's hand in a death grip. Like a crab he crawled backward. His arm muscled tightened. He could feel the weight of Carl's body now.

There was a cracking sound, but the ice did not break. Will stopped for a moment. Then he continued his slow backward crawl.

It seemed like hours. At last Will saw Carl's shoulders come up out of the water. His teeth were chattering, and he was shaking from head to foot.

"Easy does it," Will cautioned. "Lie still,

Carl. Let me pull you up and over. If you begin to thrash about, we're both gone."

Finally they reached the solid ice. Will pulled Carl to his feet and turned him toward the shore.

"I w-would h-have d-drowned if it h-hadn't been for y-you!" Carl exclaimed.

Will had no time for thanks. He had not rescued Carl from drowning to allow him to die of pneumonia. "Run!" he commanded sternly. "Run, Carl Long, or I'll give you the beating of your life!"

Louisville at Last

THE CLARK flatboat had almost reached Louisville. The current in the Ohio River seemed swifter than ever. The melting ice up the river was causing the increase in current.

Will with his brothers was standing on deck. The boat was rushing furiously downstream. The swollen waters looked dangerous.

"We had better start to pull in to shore in plenty of time," Edmund said.

"We haven't been able to land exactly where we aimed to land for the last two nights," Jonathan reminded him. "I've never been in such a strong current before."

152

"Well, we can try," said Edmund.

"And if we don't make it?" Will asked.

Jonathan looked at Will with grave eyes. "You know the answer to that question," he said.

"The Falls?"

Jonathan nodded. All the Clark brothers were silent. They knew the dangers that were hidden in those swirling waters below Louisville. The boat sped on its way. Now and then there was a thud. A cake of ice had hit the boat and bounded away. Danger rode with them on the flatboat.

"We must be about two miles from the mouth of Beargrass Creek," Richard said. "Let's try to pull in to shore."

There were four of them to man the rudder: Will, Jonathan, Richard, and Edmund. Fourteen-year-old Will was as strong as any man.

Four pairs of arms strained to turn the flatboat toward the left bank. Beads of sweat stood out on the boys' foreheads.

But the boat was caught in the mighty current. Using all their strength, they could come no closer than thirty feet to the shore.

Will's heart was pounding wildly. Had they come so far only to be dashed to pieces on the rocks below the Falls?

He thought fast. His glance fell on a coil of rope on the foredeck. "Jonathan!"

"What is it, lad?"

"We can use that rope yonder!"

"How?"

"Tie a loop in one end. Hurl it toward the shore at exactly the right moment. If it catches one of the piles that support the wharf, we'll be anchored."

Will's brothers were listening. They shook their heads. Only Jonathan looked hopeful. "It's a chance, perhaps our only one. Richard, you're the strongest. Get the rope ready."

Richard walked over to the rope. He picked

154

it up and tied a slipknot in one end. He unwound part of the rope. Then he stared downriver.

"There's an old stump near shore. If I can secure the boat to that, we'll be all right. We can get to town by land and find help to take the cargo ashore."

The flatboat traveled swiftly on. Richard braced himself and waited. The boat neared the stump. He drew back his arm. The rope whistled through the air and missed.

There was a long sigh from four throats. It seemed to come from one man. They had failed.

"Mr. Jonathan!"

York was speaking in Jonathan's ear. He had come on deck just in time to see Richard's useless effort.

"Will can do it. I know he can!"

Jonathan decided quickly. He drew in the rope and coiled it. Then he handed it to Will. "You're our last chance. Don't fail."

"There's Louisville." Edmund pointed to the little village downstream. Sixty or seventy log cabins were huddled together. From the center of the settlement rose Fort Nelson. Will knew that George himself had directed the building of that fort three years ago.

"Get ready, Will."

Will flexed his arm and rose up on his toes. His eyes were steady.

Everyone on deck stared at the little wharf.

Now the boat was barely ten feet upriver from the first post, but at least thirty feet out in the racing stream.

Will threw the rope and it sang out. The boat rushed on, but the loop circled a post. With a violent jerk the boat stopped.

The crew sprang into action. The pull of the current was strong, but all hands pulled the boat toward shore.

By now the women and girls were on deck. The sudden jolt had alarmed them. Mr. Clark and York's father helped, too. At last the boat was safely moored beside the wharf.

"Bravo, Will!" exclaimed a man's deep voice.

Will looked up. George Rogers Clark himself, tall and brown, was standing with both hands outstretched to his youngest brother. He smiled at Will. They were the same height now.

Will sighed. "We're here at last, George."

"Well done, lad!" said his brother. He turned

to a weather-beaten figure in frontier garb beside him. "Here is my brother Will of whom I've told you, Mr. Boone."

Will almost pinched himself to be certain he was not dreaming. He looked into a pair of eyes as blue as his own. This was Boone, hero of a hundred adventures. This was the greatest man—except George, of course—in Kentucky.

"I'm happy to know you, sir." Will stammered a little in his excitement.

"Good for you, Will!" said the old pioneer. "You have a steady eye and a quick mind. The West needs men like you."

Will Grows Up

Will and the rest of the Clark family were now living in their new two-story house near the Ohio River a few miles from Louisville. It was much like the house back in Virginia.

Today Will was stretched out on the ground under a tree beneath the kitchen window. The day was hot. He was glad to rest a while.

York came through the garden gate. He was carrying a load of chips for the kitchen fire.

"Stop and talk a bit," Will called. "It's dull around here."

There was the sound of a horse's hoofs pounding up the long avenue that led from the road.

159

Will sprang to his feet. He ran out into the yard where he could see better. Then he turned back to York. "It's George! Things won't be dull any longer."

George Rogers Clark strode into sight. He was in full uniform. His sword hung at his side.

"What has happened, George " Will cried. "You haven't worn a uniform in months!"

George walked quickly across the grass and placed his hands on his youngest brother's shoulders. He looked deeply into the blue eyes that were on a level with his own.

"How old are you, Will?"

"Sixteen."

The boy's heart was pounding. Something he did not understand was in the air.

"And bigger than many a man," George reflected. "Will, I want you to go with me."

"Where?" Will asked. "Not that it matters."

By now George was pacing back and forth.

Will waited without speaking. He knew he could not hurry his brother.

At last George turned and faced him. "I'm going on a dangerous mission. Most of my able-bodied men in the settlements are gathering at Louisville. Some of us may not come back. We need you, Will."

Will did not hesitate. He took a step forward. "When do we start?"

There was the ghost of a smile about George's determined mouth. "Don't you want to know where you're going?"

Will grinned. "I guess you will get around to telling me sometime. Besides, it isn't hard to guess. Indians?"

George nodded grimly. "They've burned border cabins and kidnaped settlers long enough. We shall move on Vincennes in the Northwest Territory and try to deal with them. If they do not listen, then it means war."

Will started toward the house. "Will you saddle my horse, York?" he said.

THE JOURNEY

Will Clark was a proud young fellow. He sat in the bow of the lead boat beside his brother George and looked back over his shoulder. Nearly a thousand men had assembled at Louisville to go with General Clark.

"Surely the redskins will think twice before they attack this force," Will said.

"We hope so," George answered grimly. "However, Indians do not scare easily."

The expedition traveled down the Ohio for a hundred and fifty miles. Then they came to the mouth of the Wabash River. There Will helped to load arms and provisions on a boat that would go by water to Vincennes.

"Twelve dozen long rifles, five hundredweight

of powder, and ten haunches of venison in this lot," he muttered to himself.

He felt a hearty smack across his shoulders.

"Careful planning, lad," his brother's deep voice boomed out. "That's the secret of success."

There was concern in Will's voice as he answered. "George, suppose the supplies don't reach Vincennes as soon as we do."

George shrugged his shoulders. "What's to stop them? Besides, soldiers must take some chances at times."

"But you just said careful planning——"

George laughed. "Suppose you leave the rest to me. We could never carry that heavy load overland, and we must go by land so that our scouts can report."

The journey was not exciting. The troops met three or four friendly Indians, but they were the only ones. The scouts reported that the red men were gathering in force east of Vincennes.

At last the tired men reached Vincennes. As soon as he could, Will oiled his gun and saw that it was in good shape. Then he went to George's headquarters.

"Let's give the men flapjacks for supper," he suggested to his brother. "The soldiers are very tired. Some good food will help them."

George did not answer. He was staring out the window. At last he turned around. He looked older than his thirty-four years. "The supplies haven't come yet."

Will gave a whistle of dismay. "The men are complaining, George. They're hungry. The rations have been low for several days."

"I know," George answered. "And the Indians are restless. My scouts bring me word that we should deal with them at once. What would you do in my place, Will?"

Will Clark drew himself up to his full height. His blue eyes were shining. "I would send for them. Then I would act as though I were the strongest general in the world."

"Spoken like a true Clark," declared George. "I shall do as you suggest at once."

THE PARLEY

The next day the scouts brought a message from the Indians. The red men were ready to meet with General Clark. There was excitement throughout the fort. The soldiers examined their guns. Their ammunition was low.

At dusk General Clark ordered a great bonfire lighted in the town square. Will stayed close at his brother's side. He was eager for George to be successful in treating with the Indians.

"They should be here any minute now," General Clark said. 'Will, go down to the river and see if the supply boat is in sight. We may need that powder."

Will set off at once. He wanted to stay, but he knew that a good soldier obeyed orders. He hurried to the dock and peered downstream.

Boom boom-boom! Boom boom-boom!

Will's heart beat faster. That was the sound of Indian tom-toms. Did they mean peace or war? He wished he knew.

Suddenly through the black night he saw a tiny light in the distance. As he watched it grew brighter. Could it come from a boat?

Will ran to the edge of the pier. He strained his eyes. Yes, there it was! He imagined he could see dim forms of men at the oars.

He waited impatiently for nearly an hour. The boat seemed to crawl up the river. Will thought it would never come to dock.

Finally the crew pulled up to shore and made the boat fast. Will ran out to meet the captain.

"What took you so long?" he asked.

"Mud," the man answered sourly. "Mud,

sand bars, low water, mosquitoes as big as your hand—and heat. Half the meat is spoiled."

"General Clark is holding a parley with the Indians. Will you unload tonight the provisions that aren't spoiled?"

The captain shook his head. "My men need sleep and some hot food. Let the cargo wait."

Will thought fast. If the Indians were peaceful, they would expect a night of feasting. If they were hostile, the men under General Clark would need powder. Time was passing. Someone must act at once.

His voice rang with a note of command. "I order you to transfer that cargo to General Clark's headquarters without delay."

The captain of the boat looked surprised. "Who are you?" he demanded.

Will took a deep breath. "William Clark, brother to the general himself."

The man broke into a hearty laugh. "And a

chip off the old block! Very well, lad, my men will do as you say."

Later Will pushed his way through the people who had gathered to watch General Clark deal with the Indians.

Will stopped in his tracks. The scene before him stamped itself on his memory. He would never forget it. Fifty braves in their blankets stood before George Rogers Clark. Alone he faced them. His men stood a few paces behind him. The general spoke fearlessly.

"Your shooting, robbing, and killing south of the Ohio must cease. We have traveled far to warn you. If you do not make a treaty with us and keep it, we will send many families to take your land away. We will drive you west and keep your lands forever."

There was a low murmur among the Indians. A long silence followed. Then an old chief stepped forward.

"We choose. You are the victors."

Will turned and ran back toward the provisions. There was no time to talk with George. He knew what he had to do. He must see that a feast was prepared for the Indians.

Late that night he stretched out his blanket at the foot of George's pallet.

"I hope you understand what I did, George," he began. "I did what I thought was best when I told the cooks to prepare the venison."

George laughed. "I could scarcely believe my nose when I smelled meat roasting. That venison was exactly what we needed to convince our red visitors that we want to be friends, Will," he said.

"Does this mean peace now?" Will asked.

"There is no peace where Indians are concerned," George said.

"There must be," Will insisted. "There must be, and I intend to find it."

170

The Long Trail

MORE THAN twenty years later, in May, 1804, three young men stood on the foredeck of a keelboat on the Missouri River. The boat was being pulled and rowed upriver by twenty-two men.

One of the three men, Captain Meriwether Lewis, turned to one of the others. "Captain Clark," he said, "we're on our way."

"Sir, my commission says 'Lieutenant Clark,'" Will reminded him with a grin.

"So it does," Lewis agreed. "But you're 'Captain Clark' to me. We're partners on this expedition—just as we talked about in Virginia many years ago."

171

The two men had orders from President Jefferson to explore the Louisiana Purchase all the way to the Pacific Ocean.

"And I've come along. I always told you I would, Mr. Will," said the third man, Will's servant York.

"We may meet dinosaurs," Will teased.

"And fire-breathing dragons," said Meriwether Lewis.

"And salt mountains reaching to the sky," Will Clark finished.

"You can't scare me." York grinned. "When you and Captain Lewis are along, a man forgets to be afraid."

"Stout fellow!" Will approved.

The keelboat sailed on. Behind it came two pirogues. A pirogue was made from a hollowed-out tree trunk. The red pirogue was rowed by seven *voyageurs*, or boatmen. The white one was rowed by six.

One of the French rivermen was named Cruzatte. He owned a fiddle which he loved as he would love a child. Every night he played lively tunes. The lighthearted men would dance to its music. York was the best dancer of all.

Every mile brought the explorers closer to the country of the Sioux Indians. One day the men in the boats met a trader coming downstream. He lived among the Indians.

"Will you go back with us?" Captain Clark asked. "We can't speak the Sioux language."

The trader liked the tall young man with red hair. He liked Captain Clark's quick smile and friendly ways. He liked his firm chin and commanding voice. "I will go," he said.

The expedition traveled on. The men found giant bears. They saw animals that few white men had ever seen before. There were antelopes, silver fox, bighorn sheep, mountain goats, and prairie dogs.

"When will we reach the Sioux country?" Will Clark asked the trader.

"We're nearly there."

"We must be careful," said Captain Clark. "Sometimes the Sioux are unfriendly. We'll keep the keelboat in the middle of the river."

Soon the men in the three boats began to pass Sioux villages. Captain Clark and Captain Lewis went ashore in a small boat. They sent for the Indians.

"We have come to trade with you. We were sent by the Great White Father," Captain Clark told them.

The Indians danced for the white men. Captain Clark and Captain Lewis gave them presents of tobacco, trinkets, and medals. The medals were stamped with the likeness of President Thomas Jefferson.

The red men served their visitors something hot from a huge kettle.

"What is it?" Captain Lewis asked.

"Stewed dog," the Indians told him.

"Ugh!" thought Captain Clark, though he made no comment.

It was a strange night. The Indians danced and feasted. The white men were uneasy. They kept their guns within reach and their trigger fingers ready.

Next morning they sailed on. Again and again from the shore the Sioux signaled them to stop. Captain Clark and Captain Lewis told the men to row straight ahead. They did not trust these Sioux Indians.

THE CHRISTMAS SEASON

It was late November. Nearly six months had passed since the expedition had left St. Louis. Now heavy snows were piling up and the air was very cold. The men had built a fort in which to spend the winter. They called it Fort Mandan for the Indians who lived near by.

Will Clark was sitting at a table in a snug, warm cabin. He was drawing a map of the surrounding country.

"Is it as good as the one you made for your father's birthday once when we were boys?" Meriwether Lewis asked.

Will's blue eyes twinkled. "I've had some time in which to improve. When I made that map, I didn't use the instruments we use now—a sextant or a chronometer or a compass. But I had one big advantage—Kentucky was already explored and I knew what it looked like."

There was a knock at the door. "Come in," Will called.

A dark-skinned Frenchman walked into the room. Behind him was a pretty black-eyed squaw. "I am Charbonneau," the man said. "I hear you are going beyond the Shining Mountains. Would you like me to guide you? I know the land to the west."

Clark and Lewis looked at each other. The trader who guided them through the Sioux country had turned back to St. Louis. They needed a guide badly.

"You are engaged," said the captains.

"Who is she?" asked Captain Clark. He nodded his head toward the Indian girl.

"My wife. She is a Shoshone. She was kidnaped long ago by an enemy tribe among whom I found her. She's only seventeen but strong. She speaks a little French and knows many Indian languages, too."

Clark looked at Lewis again. "This must be our lucky day. The Shoshone live in those Shining Mountains we must cross. Perhaps this girl can act as our interpreter."

"What is her name?"

"Sacagawea. It means 'bird girl.'"

Will Clark whistled in surprise. "That's too hard to say. I think I'll call you Janey." He took an immediate liking to her.

In the spring the expedition left Fort Mandan. The keelboat turned back to St. Louis. It was filled with live specimens and stuffed animals. Will knew that President Jefferson was eager to see all those things, as well as the maps and the diaries he and Meriwether had kept.

Thirty men pushed westward with Captain Clark and Captain Lewis—thirty men, one young woman, and a baby. Sacagawea now had a cunning brown Indian papoose. She called him Baptiste. Clark called him Pompey.

During the next four months the captains had many adventures to record in their diaries. One batteau with brave little Sacagawea and three

men on board nearly sank. The expedition arrived at the Great Falls of the Missouri. Then they came in sight of the Shining Mountains. Sacagawea almost lost her life in a flash flood. Will Clark rescued her.

At last they came to the land of the Shoshone. Sacagawea found her long-lost relatives. Her brother was now chief of the tribe. He said to Will Clark, "You need horses to cross the Shining Mountains. My people will trade with you."

Up, up, up went the party toward the snow-covered peaks. Sometimes they lost their way on the steep trails. They became weak with hunger. They were forced to eat two of the horses. But at last they came out on the other side of the mountains.

Sacagawea's eyes shone as she rode beside Will. "You are the first white man to cross the mountains that divide North America in two. I am proud to ride with you."

Friendly Indians gave the hungry men food. Then they directed them toward the Columbia River. The men in the canoes guided their craft into the swift waters. They raced downstream. Many times they were in danger from the rapids. But Clark and Lewis followed the *voyageurs* and led the men onward.

One day they heard a noise in the distance. It sounded like the booming of a cannon. Will Clark was happy. So was Meriwether Lewis. They knew it was the sound of breakers from the Pacific Ocean.

Before long they pitched camp near the coast. They laid claim to the land for the United States. Indians brought them word of a great whale that had washed up on the shore. Clark decided to send a party to get some of the meat.

Somehow nobody thought to ask Sacagawea if she wanted to go. She went to Captain Clark himself. "Have I not guided you across the

Shining Mountains? Have I not spoken for you to my people?" she asked.

"Why, yes, Janey."

"Have I not met danger and hunger along with you?"

"Of course, Janey. We couldn't get along without you."

Her eyes filled with tears. "Then why am I not allowed to go with the men? I, too, want to see the great fish."

Captain Clark smiled down at her. He laid his hand on her shoulder. "We didn't think. I'm sorry. Of course you may go."

Homeward Bound

ONE DAY IN March, 1806, Captain Clark said to Captain Lewis, "We should be starting home, Merne. Summer will soon be here."

"I know we should," Captain Lewis agreed. "But I hate to think of the return journey over the Shining Mountains."

"It will be hard," Will Clark answered. "But we came over and we can go back."

However, it was June before the party reached the mountains. In spite of bad weather and snow-covered trails, the men made their way slowly across the Rockies.

They stopped to rest after they crossed the

highest range. Will sat on his pack with his map propped against his knees.

"How does the map look now?" Meriwether called. He walked over to Will and stood behind him. "You certainly saved us many miles of slow water travel. I'm glad you found out about the land trails from the Indians."

"The map still has too many blank spaces, Merne," Will answered. "How I'd like to see all of this country!"

Meriwether laughed. "Not on this trip! Think how Mr. Jefferson would worry about the expedition." He pushed Will's cap over his friend's eyes. "And think how your friend Julia, in Virginia, would worry about you!"

Will grinned. "Well, then, let's fill in only some of the blank spots."

Together they worked out a plan and divided the party into three groups. Captain Lewis went due north to see what lay along Maria's River, which ran into the Missouri. Captain Clark sent several of his men to explore the Jefferson River and to see the land between there and the Mandan villages.

Clark, who had Sacagawea and little Pompey in his party, traveled toward the Shoshone country. He met herds of buffalo. He saw giant bears again. Worst of all, he and his men met hordes of fierce mosquitoes.

Will was happy when he saw Meriwether's boats land at the camp on the Yellowstone River. Then his smile disappeared. "Where is Captain Lewis?" he shouted to the men.

Cruzatte pointed to the pirogue. "He's lying in there. There was an accident today when we landed to hunt elk. Captain Lewis was shot."

Will was already running to the bank.

"It's not serious, Will," Lewis assured him. "But I'm glad we caught up with you. Even the Indians know you're a good medicine man."

Will began to clean the wound. Meriwether told about the unfriendly Indians who tried to steal his horses and about the animals and birds he had seen. "We have many rivers, mountains, and villages to add to the map, Will. We've filled in many blank places."

Near Fort Mandan, Sacagawea, her husband, and her baby left the expedition.

Clark did not want the Indian girl and her baby to go. "Let me take care of little Pompey," he begged. "I'll rear him as my own son."

Sacagawea shook her head. "He is too little. But I will bring him to you someday. I want him to be a great captain like you."

Every day brought the expedition nearer home. The time was September, 1806. Will Clark and Meriwether Lewis had been gone for more than two years. They had had adventures they would never forget. They had passed over the impassable Rocky Mountains. They had traveled four thousand miles. They had been the first Americans to cross the continent. They had laid claim to nearly half a continent.

One morning Will Clark stood on the deck of their boat. He was looking back at the rushing muddy waters of the Missouri. Meriwether Lewis was at his side.

"In a way I hate to leave it all," Will said. "I'm eager to get home. I want to see my brothers and sisters in Kentucky and my friends in Virginia. But I'm coming back. I love the frontier. The Indians are my friends. I want to see that they are treated well."

Will Clark was as good as his word. When he returned from the expedition he married Julia Hancock, who was waiting for him in Virginia. Soon he brought her back to St. Louis to live. The West was his home. He felt happiest there.

In 1813 he was made Governor and Superintendent of Indian Affairs in the Missouri Territory. Now he could help his Indian friends even more than he already had.

The Indians needed help. Few white settlers understood them or liked them.

During the War of 1812 the British tried to win the Indians to their side.

"Bring the chiefs of the tribes to St. Louis," Clark told his soldiers. "I will take them to the capital of the United States to see their Great White Father."

He traveled across the country with a large band of Indians. Many people gave them black looks. They were afraid of them.

Will Clark was kind to them. He and President Madison urged them not to fight against the Americans. Then Clark took them back to their homes.

One day in 1815 Will Clark and some other men met with chiefs from nineteen Indian tribes. They were Sioux tribes.

Governor Clark stepped forward with a smile to meet a tall red man. "Black Buffalo!"

"The redhead captain!"

Ten years before, when he crossed the continent, Clark had made friends with Black Buffalo. Today Clark and he were meeting as friends. The white men and the red men made a treaty of peace.

Governor Clark did not have an easy time. Some white men felt the Indians had no rights. Will Clark knew these men were wrong. As governor of the territory he had many questions to decide. He was busy every moment of the day.

"You have no right to those acres," he would tell white men who were trying to cheat the Indians out of their land.

"You have sold that section of land. You must not return to it," he would tell Indians who did not want to give up land they had transferred by law.

"I have heard all the evidence about those stolen horses. They must be returned to their rightful owners."

"That man sold whisky to the Indians. Put him in jail."

Governor Clark lived in a big house in St. Louis. Beside it was another house where he often met with the Indians. In this house was his Indian Museum.

Sometimes Sacagawea's little Baptiste, who was a big boy now, came to visit him. Pompey, as Clark still called him, was enrolled in a Baptist school in St. Louis. Clark and he were good friends. He would sit by the hour and listen to tales of the expedition.

"Almost as many Indians as white men come to talk with you," Pompey told Clark one day. "Why is that?"

"They know I like them," Governor Clark answered. "I have always liked them."

"Does the color of a man's skin make him different?" asked Pompey.

"Of course not," Clark said. "There are good white men and bad white men. There are good and bad red men. What matters is how a man feels and acts."

"My mother told me you are a great man and a good one," Pompey said.

"I am not great," said Governor Clark quickly. "I have tried to be good. And I like people. I like the red ones as well as the white ones, Pompey. Sometimes I wonder if I don't like them a little better. All of us, white men and red, must work together to make this country of ours great and strong."

The friendly boy in buckskins, who grew up in Virginia, had become one of the first and greatest winners of the West.

More About This Book

WHEN WILL CLARK LIVED

1770   WILL CLARK WAS BORN IN CAROLINE COUNTY,
       VIRGINIA, AUGUST 1.

The thirteen American colonies were governed
by England.

George III was King of England.

The population of the colonies was about
2,205,000.

1771–   WILL LIVED WITH HIS PARENTS ON THE CLARK
1784   PLANTATION IN CAROLINE COUNTY.

The "Boston Tea Party" took place, 1773.

The first battle of the Revolutionary War was
fought at Lexington, Massachusetts, 1775.

The Declaration of Independence was signed,
1776.

George Rogers Clark captured Vincennes, 1779.

The peace treaty with England was signed,
ending the Revolutionary War, 1783.

| 1784– | CLARK LIVED IN KENTUCKY AND SERVED PART |
| 1804 | TIME IN THE UNITED STATES ARMY. |

The Constitutional Convention met to frame the United States Constitution, 1787.

George Washington became the first President, 1789.

George Washington died, 1799.

Thomas Jefferson was President, 1801-1809.

The United States bought the Louisiana Territory from France, 1803.

| 1804– | CLARK AND MERIWETHER LEWIS EXPLORED |
| 1813 | THE LOUISIANA TERRITORY. |

Zebulon Pike explored the area now known as Kansas, Colorado, and New Mexico, 1806.

The War of 1812 was fought, 1812-1815.

"The Star-Spangled Banner" was written, 1814.

| 1813– | WILLIAM CLARK WAS APPOINTED GOVERNOR OF |
| 1837 | MISSOURI TERRITORY. |

The first account of the Lewis and Clark Expedition was published, 1814.

The Erie Canal was completed, 1825.

Samuel Morse invented the telegraph, 1835.

American settlers reached Oregon, 1836.

1838 WILLIAM CLARK DIED IN ST. LOUIS, MISSOURI,
      SEPTEMBER 1.

Andrew Jackson was President.

There were twenty-six states in the Union.

The population of the country was about
15,565,000.

DO YOU REMEMBER?

1. What trick did Will Clark and his friends try to play on Trader Jenkins?

2. What present did Will's brother George give Will when he returned from Kentucky?

3. What happened when Will and York tried to take the calf, Star, from his mother?

4. How did Will outsmart the British when he and York took horses to Coleman's Inn?

5. How did Will manage to deliver the message about hidden guns to Mr. Coleman?

6. How did Will save Randy's life when he was bitten by a water moccasin?

7. Who was the hermit of Poor Farm Hollow whom Will and York went to see?

8. How did Will and Meriwether Lewis prepare a birthday present for Will's father?

9. What happened when the Clarks stopped at an inn on their way to Pittsburgh?

10. How did Will help to get a flatboat for the family to travel down the Ohio River?

11. How did Will keep the flatboat from going over the falls at Louisville?

12. How did General George Rogers Clark make peace with the Indians at Vincennes?

13. Why did President Jefferson send Lewis and Clark into the Louisiana Territory?

14. How did the Indian woman, Sacagawea, help Lewis and Clark?

15. What important position did Clark hold when he lived at St. Louis, Missouri?

IT'S FUN TO LOOK UP THESE THINGS

1. Where is Monticello, the famous home of Thomas Jefferson, which Will Clark visited?

2. What is a flatboat, and why were flatboats once widely used?

3. Why was Pittsburgh once an important stopping place for people traveling westward?

4. What was the Northwest Territory which George Rogers Clark won from the Indians?

5. How did the United States obtain the Louisiana Territory from France?

6. What important Indian tribes formerly lived in the Louisiana Territory?

INTERESTING THINGS YOU CAN DO

1. Draw a picture of a flatboat such as the Clark family used on the Ohio River.

2. Tell who Daniel Boone was, whom Will Clark saw in Louisville, Kentucky.

3. Find out how the French came to own the Louisiana Territory.

4. Draw a map of the route which Lewis and Clark followed on their journey to the Northwest.

5. Make a list of states which have been formed from the Louisiana Territory.

6. Name several great men who helped to explore the West after Lewis and Clark.

OTHER BOOKS YOU MAY ENJOY READING

Bill Clark: American Explorer, Sanford Tousey. Whitman.

Meriwether Lewis: Boy Explorer, Charlotta M. Bebenroth. Trade and School Editions, Bobbs-Merrill.

Sacagawea: Bird Girl, Flora Warren Seymour. Trade and School Editions, Bobbs-Merrill.

Scannon: Dog with Lewis and Clark, Adrien Stoutenburg and Laura N. Baker. Scribner.

Westward the Course, Hildegarde Hawthorne. Longmans.

We Were There with Lewis and Clark, James Munves. Grosset.

INTERESTING WORDS IN THIS BOOK

architecture (är′kĭ tĕk′tŭr) : art or science of designing and erecting buildings

binding (bīn′dĭng) : obligatory, holding a person to something, as to a promise

chestnut (chĕs′nŭt) : reddish-brown, from the color of a chestnut

198

chronometer (krŏ nŏm'ĕ tẽr) : instrument designed to keep time with great accuracy

colonizing (kŏl'ŏ nīz ĭng) : act of establishing colonies

crescent (krĕs'ĕnt) : shaped like the new moon

dinosaurs (dī'nŏ sôrz) : large lizard-like animals that once lived on earth

enclosure (ĕn klō'zhẽr) : area closed in by a fence

enrolled (ĕn rōld') : placed on a list or record of membership

flexing (flĕk'sĭng) : bending

gait (gāt) : manner of walking or running, usually in connection with horses

grits (grĭts) : coarsely ground corn

gruff (grŭf) : deep and harsh, rough

hummock (hŭm'ŭk) : low, rounded hill

keelboat (kēl'bōt') : covered boat with keel but no sails, used to haul goods on rivers

magnificent (măg nĭf'ĭ sĕnt) : splendid

muffled (mŭf''ld) : deadened, dulled

murky (mŭrk'ĭ) : dark, gloomy

oilskin (oil'skĭn) : coat or cape made waterproof by oil

pallet (păl′ĕt) : small, simple bed

parchment (pärch′mĕnt) : heavy writing paper similar to sheepskin material once used for writing

pokeberry (pōk′bĕr′ĭ) : berry of the pokeweed

provisions (prȯ vĭzh′ŭnz) : supplies

quivered (kwĭv′ērd) : trembled slightly

rebel (rĕb′′l) : person opposed to authority or government

recessed (rė sĕst′) : set back

salamander (săl′ă măn′dēr) : small lizard-like animal that lives in or out of water

sawyer (sô′yēr) : person who formerly sawed wood for a living

scowled (skould) : frowned

sextant (sĕks′tănt) : instrument used in navigation to help determine latitude and longitude

shilling (shĭl′ĭng) : silver coin of England worth twelve pence, or about 14¢

specimens (spĕs′ĭ mĕnz) : samples, things chosen as examples

venture (vĕn′tŭr) : undertaking

weatherbeaten (wĕth′ēr bēt′ĕn) : tanned and worn by the weather

COLONIAL DAYS

ES OGLETHORPE, *Parks*
ES STANDISH, *Stevenson*
ER STUYVESANT, *Widdemer*
AHONTAS, *Seymour*
ANTO, *Stevenson*
GINIA DARE, *Stevenson*
LIAM BRADFORD, *Smith*
LIAM PENN, *Mason*

TRUGGLE for DEPENDENCE

HONY WAYNE, *Stevenson*
FRANKLIN, *Stevenson*
SY ROSS, *Weil*
N MORGAN, *Bryant*
AN ALLEN, *Winders*
NCIS MARION, *Steele*
RGE ROGERS CLARK, *Wilkie*
RGE WASHINGTON, *Stevenson*
AEL PUTNAM, *Stevenson*
N PAUL JONES, *Snow*
RTHA WASHINGTON, *Wagoner*
LLY PITCHER, *Stevenson*
THAN HALE, *Stevenson*
THANAEL GREENE, *Peckham*
RICK HENRY, *Barton*
UL REVERE, *Stevenson*
M JEFFERSON, *Monsell*

EARLY NATIONAL GROWTH

ABIGAIL ADAMS, *Wagoner*
ALEC HAMILTON, *Higgins*
ANDY JACKSON, *Stevenson*
DAN WEBSTER, *Smith*
DEWITT CLINTON, *Widdemer*
DOLLY MADISON, *Monsell*
ELIAS HOWE, *Corcoran*
ELI WHITNEY, *Snow*
FRANCIS SCOTT KEY, *Stevenson*
HENRY CLAY, *Monsell*
JAMES FENIMORE COOPER, *Winders*
JAMES MONROE, *Widdemer*
JOHN AUDUBON, *Mason*
JOHN JACOB ASTOR, *Anderson*
JOHN MARSHALL, *Monsell*
JOHN QUINCY ADAMS, *Weil*
LUCRETIA MOTT, *Burnett*
MATTHEW CALBRAITH PERRY, *Scharbach*
NANCY HANKS, *Stevenson*
NOAH WEBSTER, *Higgins*
OLIVER HAZARD PERRY, *Long*
RACHAEL JACKSON, *Govan*
ROBERT FULTON, *Henry*
SAMUEL MORSE, *Snow*
SEQUOYAH, *Snow*
STEPHEN DECATUR, *Smith*
STEPHEN FOSTER, *Higgins*
WASHINGTON IRVING, *Widdemer*
ZACK TAYLOR, *Wilkie*

WESTWARD MOVEMENT

BRIGHAM YOUNG, *Jordan and Frisbee*
BUFFALO BILL, *Stevenson*
DANIEL BOONE, *Stevenson*
DAVY CROCKETT, *Parks*
JED SMITH, *Burt*
JESSIE FREMONT, *Wagoner*
JIM BOWIE, *Winders*